Florencia
An
Accidental
Story

A Story Based on True Events

Douglas Bowman
John D. Mullen

Published by Dignity Publishing in partnership with Bestseller Publishing. Printed by Printing Impressions in Goleta, California.

ISBN: 978-1-946978-14-1

This publication is designed to provide accurate and authoritative information with regard to the subject matter covered. It is sold with the understanding that the publisher is not engaged in rendering legal, accounting, or other professional advice. If legal advice or other expert assistance is required, the services of a competent professional should be sought. The opinions expressed by the authors in this book are not endorsed by Dignity Publishing and are the sole responsibility of the author rendering the opinion.

Most Dignity Publishing titles are available at special quantity discounts for bulk purchases for sales promotions, premiums, fundraising, and educational use. Special versions or book excerpts can also be created to fit specific needs.

Florencia
An
Accidental
Story

Douglas Bowman
John D. Mullen

Endorsements

This is a remarkable book of compassion, recounting the true story of Florencia, a landmine victim from the bush of Mozambique, regaining her mobility and dignity, with help, transcending races and continents. Florencia's narrative stands out more than any other. Families help a relative. Friends help another friend. Who helps a stranger? And, more importantly, a stranger thousands of miles away? And yet it occurred.

John Mullen, an American businessman, and Douglas Bowman an English pastor, were living in California and read Florencia's story in a National Geographic article. Thousands read the same words and might have felt a degree of empathy. These two men, however, chose to do something. They gathered a team of high school and university students to pursue a dream to give Florencia a leg. She was brought to Bhagwan Mahaveer Viklang Sahayata Samiti (BMVSS), Jaipur, India, the world's largest organization for rehabilitating the disabled. In the next few days, she walked out like a normal person shedding her despair and miseries. Tears of joy rolled down not only from her cheeks but also of those who made this possible or watched her. It was my privilege to be one of them.

As I write, I am looking at the passport of Florencia. In just a few weeks she is arriving in Jaipur to get trained as a prosthetic technician. She will return to Mozambique to help others walk. Now, that is a miracle.

~ DR Mehta, Chief Patron,
BMVSS Jaipur Foot

I watched this story unfold firsthand. Two ordinary men, my friends, John Mullen and Douglas Bowman, had a simple idea...but it was to do something extraordinary. Their story is not only worth telling...it's a cause worth joining!! I hope it inspires you to support them in their quest to help 10,000 walk.

~ Billy Baldwin, Actor and Producer

Florencia, An Accidental Story, is an inspirational guide book for all of us to learn from and to live by. The story chronicles how human compassion, combined with commitment to purpose, can result in miraculous outcomes. I take personal pride in the role Cal Poly played in this journey, and for the courage of our students who ventured to the Jaipur Foot Clinic in India to simply 'Learn by Doing.' The result was a lesson of a lifetime.

~ Jeffrey D. Armstrong,
President California Polytechnic
State University, San Luis Obispo

I know what it's like to hear a voice saying 'you can't do this....' Most of the time, that's just a lie. The truth is, you can. I have done so many things that others thought were impossible. This story is in that category. Two guys who followed their dream. Let it inspire you and motivate you to change the world around you. It just might change you in the process!

~ Nick Vujicic, *Your Life Without Limits, Unstoppable*,
New York Times Bestselling Author,
Motivational Speaker

My professional experience as a rural doctor in the central province of Zambezia, Mozambique, during the years of war in the country, brought me in close contact with the victims of landmines, at their acute phase, with deaths, injuries and deep psychological traumas. That was a painful experience.

John Mullen and Douglas Bowman, assisted by their friends and supporters, did a wonderful job in writing 'Florencia, An Accidental Story.' Their willingness and efforts to help Florencia were faced with moments of doubt and demoralization, but these obstacles only increased their determination and resolve to succeed. They never gave up the struggle to achieve their set objective of having this rural and poor girl from Africa walking again.

Mozambique needs this prosthetic project as an instrument to bring about higher quality of life for the many. I congratulate John and Douglas for their hard work to make this project a reality. I urge each one of us to give our support for its successful outcome.

> ~ Dr. Leonardo Simão
> Former Minister of Health
> Former Minister of Foreign Affairs & Cooperation
> Republic of Mozambique

What started out as an adventure to help an 18 year old named Florencia turned into a perfect storm of creative ingenuity and waves of emotion. It started with Internships for our Multi-Media Arts and Design (MAD) Academy students. They were able to leverage media skills learned in the classroom to a phenomenal effect. *Florencia, An Accidental Story*, is a must read twenty-first century recipe for lifetime success and empowerment!

> ~ Melanie Cava, Board of Directors
> MAD Academy

Florencia, An Accidental Story, is a compelling book. It deserves to be read widely and to be enjoyed across the generations. The story captures the power that the human spirit, driven by compassion and determination, can have in the face of extreme adversity. Santa Barbara High School's very own Multi-Media Arts and Design Academy students got to experience this first hand by being a part of the inspirational story that is still happening in Mozambique and Jaipur, India. May the book and this vital effort contribute to thousands walking and a multitude of young humanitarians.

~ John Becchio, Principal,
Santa Barbara High School

About the Authors

John

The call came on the eve of my 32nd birthday. It was like a shockwave out of nowhere.

"Happy Birthday, son! You're now 32. It's your time."

My time? What could he mean by this? Does he want me to come work for him?

"Dad, it's time for what?"

"You're 32 years old and it's time for you to start your own business."

"My own business?"

A shiver went down my spine. Nothing could have prepared me for this moment of emancipation.

"Johnny, you know how it's done. You've watched me. You've seen it done.

It is my time.

That's all I needed. A serial entrepreneur had spoken, and I had his genes.

Two weeks later, JM Consulting Group was born. The delivery suite was a humble desk in the corner of a tiny apartment. The name was definitely a portend to the future, rather than a description of the present. The 'group' was me, myself, and I. This would be a classic example of 'fortune favors the brave.'

Unknown to me, the wireless cellular boom and the advent of the personal cellular phone was just around the corner. For me, the future arrived when it was announced that there would be an open competition for the airwaves of America. The winners of the wireless auctions needed consultants to locate the cell towers. I seized my chance. When I wasn't surfing at the local beaches with my kids, I rode this telecom wave and became one of the largest wireless consulting firms in the nation. Almost overnight my 'group' grew from one employee to over two hundred and fifty staff working in 40 states, and a foreign corporation, JM Consulteria, in Mexico.

A caterpillar had broken out of its cocoon and was now exploring this new-found entrepreneurial freedom.

Like my dad, I didn't stop with one company. With the 'winnings' from my telecom business, I formed JM Development and created a homebuilding business that became one of the largest boutique builders in the central coast of California. Until that point, I had reaped all the benefits of risk. I was now about to find out the darker side of risk. The housing 'bubble' of the early years of the new millennium combined with a clandestine mortgage 'affair' on Wall Street and houses foreclosed faster than a kid's soap bubbles blown into the air. They started with such optimism and fun. Suddenly every bubble was popped. Houses. Pop. Bank Loans. Pop. Banks. Pop. Companies. Pop. The only areas growing like weeds in a garden were layoffs and foreclosures.

It was economic carnage, and real estate, so often the poster child for the American Dream, was exhibit number one to illustrate the 2008 nightmare. With the same swiftness that I built my organizations in the 1990s, I found myself deconstructing these enterprises, letting go of staff, and trying to 'land the plane.'

I always enjoyed snorkeling and the sight of colorful fish, but when the global financial market is tanking, and your company is 'underwater,' it brings a sinking feeling of a very different kind. The goals are simple –

don't drown and look out for the financial sharks. Creditors in good times rapidly become predators in bad times.

I realized an important reality in the downturn. The genetic DNA code that had been implanted by my father at an early age was a passion for entrepreneurship. It had nothing to do with success. It wasn't about the money. In fact, it wasn't even dependent on any one industry. Once an entrepreneur, always an entrepreneur.

In late 2014, after many failed attempts to start up a new business I confessed to my colleagues that I had uncovered a special gift. I could now 'turn a for-profit business into a non-profit.' The statement proved to have more than a little irony. For now, I had no idea what fate might bring or the future hold. I did know myself well enough to realize it would involve a startup of some kind. I was ready for my next venture.

It was birthed on a walk with my friend, Douglas in early 2015. On that day, I had no idea where this journey would lead. Certainly, not to writing *this* book. Florencia's redemptive story needs to be told and retold in homes, villages, classrooms, coffee shops, bars, churches, and social media across the world. I count it as a privilege to accompany you, the reader, on this global adventure that touches down in Russia, America, India, and finally, Mozambique.

I hope, like me, it will touch down in a fifth place…your heart.

Douglas

While John Mullen was making millions in his thirties I was exploring other realms. At thirty-four, I was compelled to explore the temporary nature of my existence. An unforeseen illness threatened to take my life away in months rather than the years I had planned to enjoy. My wife, Fiona, was pregnant with our second child Laura. Our son, Barrie, was just eighteen months old. Through a quite remarkable set of circumstances, I experienced a complete healing.

Sickness, like hanging, 'occupies the mind wonderfully.' You can think of little else but life and, well, death.

This was the second time in my life that death had come knocking at my door. As an infant I had polio and sundry other life threatening complications. The doctors were short on bedside manner and positive words for my mum and dad. Indeed, when my son Barrie Douglas was born I asked my dad how he came up with my name, Douglas Barrie, he said, "Oh I got the name for your death certificate, the doctor mentioned you were not likely to survive the day, so I got to my work and saw my boss' name and thought, yes that will do." Unlike mum, the harsh realities of life had produced in my dad an inveterate pessimist.

Mum was of an altogether different kind - after all her maiden name was Smiley. Words like determined, persistent, optimistic, faith and possible fit hand-in-glove with her nature. She also knew the value of bombarding heaven with her request for divine intervention. Heaven did. Intervene. The visitor at the door of my life was turned away. I lived, walked, ran, spoke, and thought. All of this was in sheer defiance of the doctor's wisdom. I say defiance because it speaks of the very human side of the intervention, mum's fortitude and the I'll-show-them-the-impossible focus.

It took me a long time, a very long time, to learn that vulnerability is a strength not weakness.

Thank God for sports, otherwise I might have had no friends at school. I played on every team. In fact, I would have played on the girl's hockey team if it had been allowed. It was not only fun, it kept me from loneliness. Besides, I was pretty good at many of the games. It was at school that a teacher took advantage of my shyness away from the soccer or rugby field.

At thirteen I was abused. I'm not sure how it all works except to say it shut down part of my soul when it should have been emerging.

Sport and a church youth group provided an escape but not a solution. In many ways I dismissed the obvious emotional impact and trauma of the incidents. Sometimes, we bury our living wounds and give them a premature funeral. But, when we do not realize the depth of our shame and assassinate it, we unconsciously lock ourselves away from the uninhibited life that is available to the vulnerable. Success, beauty, degrees, faith and relationships merely provide a cover.

Why share this here, in these very public pages? Because it may help you, the reader, understand who it is writing with my very good friend, John. It may also give you an insight into some of the *'why did he do this'* question. It may also encourage you to know that the 'whole people' who have never discovered their brokenness have little to offer the poor and broken of our world. Only those who have lived in the world of suffering, who know what it is like to be at the end of their rope or be with those who are, can truly offer empathy and be driven to assist them without being a condescending do-gooder, all platitudes offered in an undercurrent of pride. They too could be free if they let out some secret of their own to one close to them.

So, this is the quite different friend of John the Entrepreneur. God only knows how on earth we got together and arrived at this place with this story, almost too fantastic to be true, except it is.

What would I leave you with at the outset of this story? A question to live with while you read. It changed my world.

'What would you do, if you were ten times more bold?'

Either write something worth reading,
or do something worth writing

~Benjamin Franklin

Table of Contents

Part 3: Goodness Blooms

Foreword

Dear Reader,

This book is about profound human compassion and solidarity, a true compassion which doesn't stop with empathy and shed tears, but leads to action.

As a Mozambican citizen and former President of Mozambique, I am well placed to confirm that our country went through very difficult times in its recent past, where a war situation co-existed with natural disasters (such as cyclones and droughts) and landmines, severely damaging the country, then considered the poorest nation on the planet.

It took us hard work, perseverance and faith to put an end to the war, which caused about 1 million deaths, 4 million Internal Displaced People and 4 million refugees, most of them in the neighboring countries of Malawi, Zimbabwe, South Africa, Swaziland, Zambia and Tanzania. Economic and social infrastructure was extensively destroyed, such as bridges, factories, sugar plantations, schools, and health care facilities, among others.

The war brought an untold level of suffering to Mozambicans. In particular, to rural people like Florencia, not only by its direct impact on their lives, but also by killing and maiming their relatives, friends, colleagues and other co-citizens as well. Furthermore, the war destroyed their means of living, making them dependent on external aid to physically survive. People who were normal citizens, taking care of their families, participating in the affairs of their communities and nation were reduced to beggars during many years.

Eventually, on October 4, 1992, the Government of Mozambique and the then rebel group RENAMO signed a peace agreement, known as the Rome Accord, which ended the war in the country, thus initiating an era of peace and stability.

The suffering of the people of Mozambique was worsened by cyclones, severe droughts and other natural disasters. Indeed, in the year 2000, Mozambique was hit by the worst floods in its history, with more than 700 lives lost and damages estimated at US $500 million dollars. Natural disasters can be more destructive than wars.

These floods happened at the very time when people were struggling to recover and rebuild their lives, enjoying the dividends of recently won peace. Therefore, when John Mullen and Douglas Bowman visited Mozambique for the first time, in 2002, the country was still recovering from the floods, heading to resume the reconstruction of the regions destroyed by both the war and the floods. During their visit the two gentlemen witnessed the conjugated impact of poverty, cyclones and landmines on the populations. It was during those moments of trial that we, Mozambicans, much appreciated and valued human solidarity.

The landmines, these unique tools of war, were planted in Mozambique in three different historical periods; the struggle for independence, the acts of war committed by the then minority regimes of Ian Smith in then Rhodesia (today Zimbabwe) and Apartheid South Africa in Mozambique and during the armed conflict opposing RENAMO to the Government of Mozambique. Initially estimated at between 1 and 2 million, the landmines were from different origins and planted by different actors in the conflicts the country went through. They made victims (between deaths and injuries) during the military battles and well after the war was ended, but also prevented the use of large areas of land for economic activities, in particular, farming. That is why many call them immortal weapons. Florencia is one of those victims, brilliantly portrayed by John and Douglas.

For these reasons, Mozambique played an active role in the negotiation of the agreement to ban anti-personnel landmines, known as the Ottawa Treaty. Furthermore, Mozambique hosted the First Meeting of the State Parties of the Ottawa Treaty, in May 1999. This active participation assisted the country to set up and implement a vigorous demining program, which had started in 1993, with the support of the United Nations, during the implementation of the Rome Accord. The Mozambican demining program ended in September 2015, when the country was declared free of known minefields.

In this marvelous book, John Mullen and Douglas Bowman were able to capture the essence of the different facets and dimensions of suffering brought about by landmines. Florencia represents all the victims of these weapons. The recalling of their first visit and research led them to Florencia and implanted in them the urge to help this young woman.

To that end, they created the charity organization HOW International (Help One Walk), which not only mobilized good will and support in the United States, but also went on to establish a partnership with the prestigious and well known Indian organization Jaipur Foot (BMVSS). Jaipur Foot generously provided a prosthesis to Florencia, and more importantly, is helping create the conditions in Mozambique to assist more than 10,000 people in need of these artificial means of compensation. It is further heartening to know the personal interest of DR Mehta in the initiative, not only because of his recognized professional experience, but also the philosophical and moral values he is bringing into the project.

Aderito Ismael and his Mozambican organization, RAD, which stands for *Rede de Ajuda à Deficiência* (and can be translated as Deficiency Support Network), played a critical role in bringing this story to fruition. He took several days off from his work with Handicap International and travelled up the coast of Mozambique to deliver the news to Florencia that she could receive a prosthetic leg. He is one of the most dedicated and admirable Mozambican citizens to the cause of the victims of landmines, a man of whom the country is exceedingly proud. It's no wonder this book is dedicated to Aderito de Jesus Ismael.

This is a book written with passion and compassion, based on values and full of lessons of life and hope of a better future. Their authors tell us this future is a real possibility for the survivors of landmines like Florencia. They call each one of us into action, to express our solidarity by participating in the building of the future of others. Let us respond, "Yes" to their call.

Maputo, April, 6 2018

Joaquim Alberto Chissano
Former President of the Republic of Mozambique

Prologue

Sweat poured down the crevices of her brow, she clenched her fist, and the face grimaced with a sharp pain that sent a thousand needles up the side of her body. The crutch had failed again. While attempting to collect water for her son, Florencia had the stark reminder that things were not as easy as they used to be. Her crutch had slid on the dusty road and gravel, which would lead her to the water. Each day brought a battle of its own, and today was no different.

The well was almost completely dry, and so was Florencia's spirit. How much longer could she go on trying to accomplish the seemingly insignificant, but daunting tasks? Who would provide for Guildo, her beautiful boy? Many days Florencia could move past these gnawing questions of doubt and despair. Today, the landmines of the mind were winning.

Unbeknownst to her, the silent cries were heard, way beyond the visible horizon. Two men, navigating through their own struggles, would stop for her. A team of complete strangers would work collectively and selflessly to provide help for the young woman they had yet to meet. Some may call it fate, or providence, maybe chance.

From where Florencia stands, it has all been, really, quite, accidental.

Part 1

INNOCENCE CRUSHED

Chapter 1

The Garden of Evil

Farewell happy fields...
Hail, horrors, hail.
~John Milton, Paradise Lost

It begins with a question.
How do you maim?
You create a device...

The clock struck 5:00 am and the buzzer began its annoying routine. A swift hand silenced the sound. The 42-year-old man lifted the cover and immediately the bone-chilling air challenged his resolve. The air never won.

He dragged his reluctant, still warm-as-toast, legs into action. He swiveled out of the bed and planted his woolen socks on the cold concrete floor. A crack in the heavy velvet-like window covering revealed the faint glimmer of a street light. The sun would finally thaw out close to noon. He groped in the dark to find his uniform neatly draped over a chair.

With great dexterity and speed he secured his trousers and stepped into the bathroom.

Just two minutes had passed when his petite wife of fifteen years swept aside the last remnants of the many layers of sub-zero protection. She quickly put on her thick non-designer housecoat and moved to the kitchen area of the room to make some tea. Like an actor following a script, she played her part well. Actually, it was a daily drama of the inhabitants in this desolate tundra.

Nikolai dipped his razor into the lukewarm water and shaved the day-old stubble. How he wished he could afford an electric shaver. Unfortunately, a beard was not an option. Irena disapproved. She had decided he would either look like an orthodox priest or a Siberian prisoner. Nikolai wasn't that holy, and besides, he never broke the law.

It was only a few paces from the bathroom to the main room of this simple square box. What made this square room a home was the carefully placed photographs displayed behind the glass doors in an ancient, heirloom cabinet. Images of weddings, holidays, babies, and men in uniform brought color against this nondescript room.

Two folding chairs formed bookends to the poker-sized square table. Nikolai carefully placed his body on the rickety frame. It groaned, and Irena breathed a sigh of relief. The chair had survived to live another day. Nikolai downed his tea and ate a bowl of kasha. Irena held his overcoat in front of the radiating oven.

At exactly 5:30 am a horn blew from down below in the street. His ride was waiting. Nikolai kissed Irena goodbye. He ran down the three flights of stairs, pushed the metal door open and greeted the bitter tundra winds that penetrated through every layer of his clothing. It would be at least twelve hours before the bus returned. He felt lucky it came every day and was always on time. The factory bus was packed to the brim. Nikolai made his way to the back and stood, surrounded on all sides by his co-workers.

The bus slowly approached the factory and the passengers began to tighten their scarfs, adjust their gloves, and pull down their fur earflaps of their ushanka. Each man showed his photo identification to the guard as they passed through the security gates. Nikolai remembered his first day on the job. 'There are guards everywhere at this place and with serious looking weapons.' The building perfectly mirrored the weather. This sterile structure had no redeeming value other than housing the machinery and men necessary to fulfill its intended purpose.

Nikolai was exceptionally skilled for the intricate work demanded on his assembly line. Most of his colleagues made two observations about him, he had great respect for the work that he was doing, and yet he gave the impression that he could do it blindfolded. It was for these reasons that new members would go through rigorous training under his mentorship. The work in this remote factory town in the urban white wilderness of Russia demanded precision of the highest order. Anything less could have disastrous results.

For twelve years Nikolai had faithfully served the Collective. He was not the kind of man who sought promotion or influence – that carried far too much political baggage and further intrusiveness into one's life. No, Nikolai had life just the way he wanted it. The winter could get him down as it wore on endlessly, month after month. Irena felt the same but her job in a nearby shop gave her some decent conversations with the locals.

Nikolai's one salvation was his love for ice fishing in winter. Swigging vodka from his hip flask, snacking on smoked sausage, his favorite brown bread and the thrill of a bite on the end of his line broke up the weeks of relentless cold. It was strange how he never thought about the frigid outdoors when he was out in this vast, frozen desert doing what he loved. Actually, although not a religious man, at times he sensed a kind of spiritual, almost supernatural, wonder in this landscape. Some might regard the same space as a wasteland. Not Nikolai. For him, it was a priceless gift. In some ways, the ice cathedral was his church.

This particular Monday morning the Collective assigned Sergei, a new worker, to Nikolai's assembly line. It always amazed Nikolai that young men came seemingly devoid of the necessary talent or dedication, and yet, in a few weeks, they began to look fairly accomplished. Nikolai had a unique personality that combined confidence with humility. That probably accounts for the fact that he was almost universally admired by these apprentices.

One thing that never surprised Nikolai was a question every new man eventually asked. The 'Question' would not come up on the first day—nobody would venture into this forbidden territory, even if they were desperate to ask. But, give them a few days of conversations, over lunch or a tea break, and, sure enough, the words would spill out.

Nikolai noticed that Sergei was a fast learner. He was very impressed with his protégé. However, in this line of work speed without focus could prove fatal. Later that same week Nikolai inspected some of Sergei's work. He had become too confident for his own good. One afternoon a 'situation' occurred. He noticed that Sergei had made an error in this painstaking process. "Sergei, stop what you're doing. You put the firing pin in the wrong way. Don't you realize that it could explode, and we could both be dead?"

Immediately the blood drained from Sergei's face. He felt a sudden weakness in his knees and pulled back from the workbench.

Nikolai realized this was going to be a vital teaching moment for his young recruit.

"Ok. Let's start from the beginning and go through the assembly step by step."

Nikolai disassembled the PMN, and they were now looking down at the small disc-shaped object, about the same size of a saucer. Alongside, were ten components that were designed to fit perfectly inside the casing. "Sergei, you must respect the process. Execution is more important than speed. We do this because it means we value our colleagues' lives. Nobody here works in isolation."

He stood next to Sergei, both wearing their rubber gloves and their protective acrylic shields in the lowered position. Sergei could feel the palpitations of his heart as beads of sweat formed on his forehead. Nikolai was in perfect control as he assembled the unit with surgical precision.

Nikolai took the green casing and within minutes had installed the spring-loaded striker, stab detonator, and horizontal fuse. He secured the fuse with a safety pin to prevent the striker from moving forward. He then put the firing pin in its 'proper' vertical position and set the arming key which protruded from the case. He began building the cylindrical layers which would fit onto the casing beginning with the spring plate, then the pressure plate, the pressure plate cover, and sealing it with the closure ring. He turned the device upside down and unscrewed the filler plug. He then placed a cone into the plug and poured exactly 250 grams of explosive powder into the cavity. He replaced the plug and the unit was now complete.

By now Sergei was suitably chastened and the whole situation merely heightened his admiration for Nikolai's expertise and collegial, rather than condescending, attitude. Sergei would never forget Nikolai's decisive words, almost as powerful as the device, 'Execution is more important than speed.'

Nikolai thought it wise to continue the conversation. It would ensure their relationship had not been damaged by the serious tone he had taken. He shifted the subject to more pleasurable topics such as ice hockey, the new liberal trends in Russian politics, and vacationing in the Baltics.

The PMN, had been appropriately nicknamed the 'Black Widow.' Its namesake, the deadly spider, is known to hide in dark crevasses and strike a fatal blow when provoked. Black Widows are known for 'legs.' The spider has eight. The PMN has no legs. Its mission is to remove legs.

Nikolai's mind wandered to a time some years earlier when his superiors held a meeting in which he had been instructed about the intent of this device...

'The Black Widow is meant to maim, not kill. The 250 grams of explosive powder are five times as powerful as similar landmines. It is a brilliant tactical ordnance! It is intended to blow off a leg and keep the enemy preoccupied with infrastructure repair and stretch medical resources.'

Sergei began to have one of those moments where the full realization of what he was actually doing seemed to have a profound effect on him. Nikolai underlined in a matter of fact way that the Black Widow needed to work perfectly. Maybe it was those last few words, 'work perfectly' that ignited Sergei's thoughts that he had hastily dismissed when applying for the job. It was time. Time for 'The Question.'

"Don't you ever think about what we are making and what they are going to do?"

Nikolai didn't look up. A realist always finds it impossible to look into the eyes of an idealist. It takes one back to a time too painful to remember. "Thinking will drive you to a place you don't want to go. A living hell. Not even vodka can help you there."

The Black Widow with serial number 311-1 joined the rest of the devices that were boxed and ready to ship. A few minutes later they were loaded in the transport truck to St. Petersburg on their way to their final destination.

A blaring fog horn of a sound reverberated through the whole factory indicating the end of the shift. Nikolai and Sergei removed their protective gloves and visors. They had missed the five hours of daylight that had existed during their shift. It was always a strange sight to see several hundred men with faces bent down into the wind fighting to get to their bus. This particular night was a quite balmy February evening at -18 Celsius. Some days it could be -40 Celsius to an extreme of -50 degrees Celsius.

One of the peculiar pastimes of many workers in the factory was to check out the newspaper for the temperatures in other parts of the world. In many ways, it was kind of a masochistic thing to do, but with a glass of vodka in hand one could always close one's eyes and drift off to Africa's sunny climes and sandy beaches. Whenever the day came that a recruit would ask 'The Question,' it took more than a couple of shots of vodka before the novice worker could forget the poisoned fruit of his labors and dream of a beach in Africa.

Chapter 2

Medical Kits

Oh what a tangled web we weave
When first we practice to deceive.

~Sir Walter Scott

The Russian Freighter slowly made her way into the harbor to dock in Maputo, Mozambique, 7000 miles from the Arctic Circle. This was definitely not the tundra. Even the water temperature was +29 Celsius. The air, at a suffocating +33 Celsius, was made all the more uncomfortable by the 90% humidity. These palm tree–lined beaches would have brought a big Russian grin to Nikolai's face, and it would have redefined his idea of 'balmy' weather.

It wasn't long before the Captain of the Malatov was hot, unhappy and frustrated. He was well used to port bureaucracy and the necessary paperwork, but this was his first taste of 'African time.' The lengthy wait for customs clearance afforded the Captain an opportunity to scan the ship's manifest one last time. One line caught his attention and brought a raised eyebrow and a wry smirk: 'Quantity: 500, Description: 'Medical Kits.' The irony was not lost on him.

Black Widow 311-1 was beginning to sweat. She needed a cool, dark space to hibernate.

In the headquarters of the Frelimo Government, Colonel Vasco Santos dialed the international code and the private number of his contact.

A man with a deep baritone voice picked up and answered, "DOH-bryh-VYEH-chuhr!" There was no apparent warmth in his brusque 'good evening.' It was actually as icy as the Russian winter.

Santos sat up at attention and repeated the English phrase that was their secret code.

"The Black Widows have landed."

All Santos heard next was a brusque, "Good!" There was a click and the line went dead.

The security barrier was in the horizontal position. The Russian ZIL 131 Military Cargo Transport slowed down, grinding its gears to a complete stop. Light rain was falling on the dust-coated windshield as the driver handed his papers to the guard.

"Here are our orders."

The guard looked at them briefly and walked to the back of the vehicle, lifted up the canvas flap and peered inside.

Stacked neatly like canned goods were fifty boxes marked with black stamped letters,

'MEDICAL KITS'

The guard quickly lost interest in the cargo and made his way back to the covered protection of his booth. He signed the papers and handed them back to the driver.

"Boa Noite." He waved them on.

The transport vehicle turned onto Highway 1 to begin the torturous journey up the coast of Mozambique. In the middle of a civil war no one knows how long it will take to travel anywhere in the country or guarantee a safe arrival.

Fernando leaned down and flipped the switch for the windshield wiper. Three or four seconds later a highly offensive screeching sound could be heard from the lone wiper blade. Rain and dirt created a smeared surface.

"Fernando, turn it off! We can't see a thing!"

Two seconds later, the churning stopped and Fernando reached back to grab a sponge and yesterday's newspaper. He pulled the vehicle to the side of the road and got out and went to work to get the shield clean. Unfortunately, the rain had stopped.

As he got back in the cab, Fernando shifted into gear and uttered the now familiar words, "I guess the nine-year drought is not going to be over tonight.

Alexei responded, "I don't know how they survive in the villages." "Well, whether it's the war or the drought, many of them have fled to Malawi, Zimbabwe, Tanzania, or South Africa. I reckon the ones in South Africa got the best deal because they've got water, food, and decent shelter."

Eight hours later, they passed through Xai-Xai and came to a government checkpoint at the entrance to the bridge over the Limpopo. Again, they presented their papers and were waved on.

Fernando remarked to Alexei, "Like many parts of Africa, life in Mozambique is either 'feast or famine.' Actually, it would be more accurate to say, 'floods or famine.' The crops may be wasted under two meters of water or, like now, the ground is bone dry and unusable. Tonight, most people just want a good soaking of rain – not a flood."

Fernando and Alexei were glad that they lived in Maputo, even if it was expensive, at least you could still buy food.

Once they passed through the Frelimo check point, Alexei tightened his grip on the AK-47. The Renamo Rebels could be anywhere. They didn't set up checkpoints. They would ambush any vehicle indiscriminately, and Frelimo was their primary target.

Just under two hours later, the orange hue of the sun crowned over the dashboard. Sunrises in Africa are momentous. In Mozambique, they are legendary. By now, the windshield had collected a significant amount of dust, sand, and mosquitos. This was a painful joy. A spectacular beauty that had become a blinding light.

Inharrime was one of the many small towns dependent on agriculture particularly cashew nut farming. Mozambique was the global leader of cashew nuts during the early 1970's. The civil war and ban on cashew nut exports had all but crushed this industry and harmed the local and national economy.

"Alexei, can you open the flask of coffee? There are plenty of rolls, eggs, and bananas in the lunch box. That should keep us going until we reach Inhambane. If there are no 'issues' on the road we should make it in under three hours. Our base there always gives us a great lunch."

Alexei was starving. He had brought nothing with him, so this was music to his ears.

Alexei, finishing his second roll, was beginning to think that there really was something to this 'married' life. Maybe he should follow Fernando's advice and start looking for a prospect. Fernando had given him some tips, the most important being, 'taste her cooking'. On that score Alexei knew, first hand, that Fernando had made a *maravilhoso* choice – his best meal of the week was the Sunday lunch that Gabrielle, Fernando's wife, set before him.

In stark contrast, the war zone of Mozambique brought other thoughts that consumed the mind. In a war, the darkness pervades even when the sun is shining bright. A nagging thought lurks, 'will I survive to live another day?' It haunts. It hunts. It looks for any weakness in the mind. Parents worry. On the other hand, watching their children play and hearing their laughter is a healthy distraction. There is the constant struggle to highlight the beauty of this tropical paradise rather than recite the stark tales of torment and ugliness.

At least during the decade-long fight against the colonial forces of Portugal, the purpose was clear: freedom and self-government. Civil war adds extra, devastating dimensions – fellow citizens battle each other and villages and regions become zones of hate and burial grounds of children and their parents. Millions only survive by escaping into a neighboring country. Bitterness and resentment in the hearts simply blind a nation to what is happening before their very eyes. Just two years after the colonial war a generation's once bright future fades and disappears with every passing year.

The war ignores every attempt to bring the madness to a conclusion. It has an energy that defies all rational thinking. The nations of the world don't have Mozambique's interests. No, they are all like scheming chess players and Mozambique's future is merely an expendable pawn. After nine years the only 'fruit' of this war is the maimed who lie helpless, the starvation that murders, poverty that grows faster than the weeds in the empty fields, and once great historic buildings that are no longer standing, or are a pale shadow of their former glory.

In the fields and villages of Inhambane it did not need a guided tour to begin to take in the scorched earth methods of both sides. Alexei remarked to Fernando that it felt like the skirmishes were intensifying rather than abating. He was right. The period from 1986 to 1988 would see some of the fiercest fighting and most shocking crimes of any war, in any part of the globe. In their body language both took on a vigilance that was almost tangible. Fernando had heard Frelimo radio reports of just how evil both the Renamo were and the devices that they used in the villages.

"They don't fight fair, those ruthless rebels," Alexei said with an air of complete innocence. Fernando agreed – their men would never resort to such things. The Russian truck pulled into the Frelimo base, Fernando slowly got out, stretched and tried to get some life into his road-weary buttocks. Alexei went through the same routine on his side of the cab. It had been a long, long drive. Some new recruits walked over from the mess and began, carefully unloading the 'Medical Kits.' Once the goods were safely counted and transferred to the waiting area Fernando and Alexei headed straight for the shower – a luxury in this drought-plagued land. It was limited to three minutes but that was long enough for the two men to reappear in the mess hall refreshed and ready to eat. If one couldn't dine in the finest places in Maputo, and only the head honchos of government, industry and the military could do that, then the food in the army was almost worth the price of enlistment. Plenty of people in the villages would have given anything to be so fortunate.

Two soldiers reported for duty at 11:00 pm. This would be a clandestine operation. They each carefully loaded five Black Widows into their packs. Their military backpacks would return empty within ninety minutes. One of the men caught the devious look in the other's eye and he responded with a devilish grin. The destination for their diabolical work that night was a tree-lined headland above the Indian Ocean. The object would be to ensure no Renamo could take that hill. If they did, movements of the Frelimo forces would be vulnerable to attack.

The villagers of Macachula were sleeping in their huts and oblivious to the unwanted guests. At the crest of the hill a series of Black Widows were placed in the ground, with meticulous care, ten meters apart. It was Frelimo's Renamo surprise.

The soldiers signaled each other. No words were necessary. One held up one finger. His comrade showed three. They moved further down the hill to establish a second line of defense. With the stealth of professional soldiers, they slithered like snakes, weaving in and out of the dying crops. The slim pickings from these symbols of starvation would leave stomachs empty and, for some, the bloating signs of impending death. The khaki cloth of their uniform soaked up the dampness of the dew forming on the ground. With the wave of a hand, one of the soldiers pointed to the well-worn path. This would be the final resting place for the last four Black Widows.

The soldier with three mines noticed that one of them was an extra powerful Black Widow. It was a booster mine. He remembered that this type of mine wouldn't merely maim, but instantly kill its victim. He planted that one first. Beside the path, the soldier with one mine put his hand into his bag and retrieved his final Black Widow. Against the dark of night, he saw the almost luminous numbers on the plastic green casing...'311-1.' The metal trowel pierced the sandy soil at an angle of approximately 30 degrees. It dug to a depth of 10 centimeters and carefully cleared out a circular area of soil to receive 311-1. In one decisive maneuver, he twisted the arming key and pulled it from the base. Internally, a series of orchestrated movements took place in perfect harmony. The detonator housing was set free, the slider spring drove it with force across the shaft, and it locked into place.

All that was required now was a few swift movements of the trowel and 311-1 was hiding, waiting – ready or not. Especially for those who weren't seeking.

It was just a matter of time, and there was plenty of time...

Chapter 3

Hide and Seek

The bliss of being young and innocent:
we daydreamed without pain, without fear, without loss.

~Bo Bennett

The white bird glided effortlessly across the blue canopy. A little girl strained her eyes until the bird disappeared into the clouds. *Imagine, what would it be like to sit on the back of one of those birds?*

A figure shot out from behind a cashew tree. There standing before Florencia was a young boy. Filipe had gleaming ivory teeth. His ebony skin glistened under the baking hot sun. His wiry frame showed an absence of flesh on his bones.

As he stood alongside Florencia you could be forgiven for thinking that she was his older sister, yet they were the same age. These two were inseparable. They spent hours each day playing games, laughing, chasing one another, and filling their stomachs with cashew nuts.

Behind Filipe's smile lay the heart of a temperamental prankster. He could frustrate Florencia if a particular game wasn't going his way.

"Hey, Florencia, do you want to play hide-and-seek?"

Without thinking, Florencia placed her hands over her eyes and began to count. 1..2..3… Filipe interrupted, "Not so fast!" He calculated the time it would take to scurry to the far hut.

At the count of ten, Florencia opened her eyes, and before she could utter, "ready or not here I come," she heard a familiar voice.

It was her mother. "Florencia, what do you need to remember?" "It's okay mama. You've told us a thousand times. We can't go beyond the path."

"And why is that Florencia?" Her mother wanting reassurance. "Because there are dangerous things in the ground." Florencia replied.

At times, her mother could be very stern and take on a serious demeanor, especially when it was a matter of life or death. Florencia and her mother were no strangers to tragedy. When Florencia was just three years old her father died in a car accident. A difficult life immediately became all the more fragile and serious. But most of the time her mother was fun. Especially those times when Florencia worked with her, hoeing the ground, cooking, washing the laundry, or simply gathering firewood.

Having calmed her mother, Florencia put her muscular legs in motion and sprinted across the ground to Filipe's hideout. She flew with such grace and power, like an Olympian. All of Mozambique was still talking about their most famous Olympic gold medalist, Maria Mutola. Two years earlier in 2000, Maria had won the 800-meter race in Sydney. She would compete in a total of six Olympic games. She became extremely wealthy by Mozambique standards and dedicated herself to helping underprivileged children in education and athletics. Such was her physical prowess that Maria took up professional soccer for a season following her running career. All these dreams might be future possibilities for Florencia. But at this moment, she was using her strong legs to pursue Felipe, who was nowhere to be seen.

Florencia knew that Filipe had a problem. He could not stay in any one place for more than ten seconds without peeking.

She stood still behind a large bush like a lioness in tall African grass awaiting the appearance of her prey. Her ears perked as she scanned the landscape for any movement. Sure enough, she looked up and spied two dark brown eyes and a black curly tuft of hair, not quite hidden in the branches of a mafura tree.

"Tag! You're it!" Florencia wasn't quite gloating but she enjoyed a sense of conquest.

With all the running she was looking forward to catching her breath and resting in her own secret hiding place. Felipe had yet to find it. Florencia always waited until Felipe was out of sight before she reappeared at the center of the village and proudly declared, "You couldn't find me!"

Florencia settled into her comfortable cavern. Felipe was scavenging to find her in all his usual places. This time, Felipe would not suffer defeat. "Florencia…. Felipe, lunch!" It was Felipe's mother. The game came to an abrupt end. The two friendly warriors strolled to the mud hut and immediately recognized the familiar aroma of beans and rice being cooked over a fire. They plumped their bodies down on the brown straw mat and within minutes were consuming their meal. Florencia did not believe in chewing or tasting. She shoveled down her food at an astonishing rate. Felipe was not thin without reason, he always struggled to eat even half of his bowl. His mother said it was on account of his difficult first few months in life when she had problems feeding Felipe. During lunch, Florencia's mind returned to muse on the wonder of the little bird high in the sky. "Why can't I fly like that bird? It would be amazing!"

The Big White Bird leveled off at 32,000 feet. The man sitting in seat 22B had a profound look of relief on his face.

His friend Douglas leaned over and whispered with a hint of sarcasm, "John, can you see the road to Beira below?"

"Yes, I'm so glad to be up in the air looking down, particularly THAT road. We are well out of harm's way."

Douglas laughed, "Honestly, I'm a little disappointed." "Are you serious?" "Actually I am…yes, somewhat."

21

The middle-aged men had been deep in conversation since LAM Flight 104 had departed from Maputo to Beira.

This was an unusual trip for John Mullen. As a successful businessman, he was used to flying first-class, staying in five-star hotels, and dining at the finest Michelin Star restaurants. John wondered how he ended up in one of the poorest countries in the world. The answer to that question could be traced back to a chance encounter with the fast-graying Englishman in 23A, Douglas Bowman. If it was unusual for John to find himself in Mozambique, it was almost inconceivable for Douglas to imagine himself having John as a travel companion.

Two years earlier, John and Douglas' worlds collided on a soccer field in Santa Ynez, California. It was really quite accidental. Laura Bowman and Nicole Mullen were teammates on their All-Star soccer team. When it comes to a soccer match, Douglas is in constant perpetual motion. Even if he's on the sidelines he sees himself as the twelfth player. You can hear him long before you see him. He shouts encouragement to players, corrects the referee for 'obvious errors of judgment,' and wills the ball into the net. On the other hand, John is always on the clock. Standing on the other side of the field with a cell phone glued to his ear and occasionally giving a token wave offering with his pinkie.

For John, there were two kinds of strangers; those who didn't deserve any acknowledgment and those who intrigued him. Douglas offered a little of both. John had raised his eyebrows when Nicole calmly delivered the shocking news that Mr. Bowman was a pastor of a local church. He immediately exclaimed; 'It must be a three-ring circus!' Yet, after two or three games, John found Douglas more engaging than annoying and invited him to coffee.

Little did either of them know that a double tall latte would change their lives forever. Not long after that caffeine-infused dialogue, Douglas celebrated his 50th birthday. Other than the obvious importance of this milestone, the occasion proved to be a decisive moment in Douglas' life. He resigned from his position and joined the ranks of the unemployed.

To commemorate his birthday, John wrote him a check for $5,000. It was an investment into his future and an affirmation of their rapidly developing friendship.

For nine months the check slept on the top of Douglas' chest of drawers. It didn't move. There was a greater purpose for this gift, and it had not yet been put to work. Instinct finally met reality with an opportunity for Douglas to travel to Mozambique with a faith-based humanitarian mission. He felt it was important to share the news with John. Maybe it was a 'British' thing, but it led to a 'coffee-shed' moment at Starbucks.

"John, is it okay with you if I use the money to go to Mozambique?" John quickly affirmed, "Of course, it's your check."

Douglas didn't really have much to disclose as far as details, merely that he just knew he had to go.

"And one more thing, John, why don't you come? We could use the other half of the money and go together."

John made calculated decisions based on sound factual evidence. What came out of his mouth next was surprising, even for him.

"I'm definitely coming. But, I don't need the other half. Keep it. By the way, when is this trip?"

"Six weeks from today. The beginning of August."

John froze. How could he put his business dealings in order, so he could make the trip? There might not be enough hours in the day to complete all tasks before him. He, however, felt a curious longing to shake up his 'normal' and seize the moment.

John, who had appeared to be momentarily channeling Indiana Jones, soon reclaimed his rightful role as a CEO and directed Douglas, "Okay. Deposit your check and book the tickets."

Above the tell-tale drone of the engine, the pilot interrupted the chatter of the passengers and made his announcement, "Ladies and gentlemen we are beginning our descent into Beira and will be arriving on time in thirty minutes."

John and Douglas continued their lively exchange over the aborted road trip.

"Douglas, the truth is, there could be a landmine in *any* field down there. We could be flying over one right now..."

———

Florencia patiently waited for Felipe to finish his bowl. She spotted a small rounded stone beyond her foot. She raised her leg to hover above the stone and carefully lowered her toes making a slight impression in the soft sand. Florencia was an expert at this maneuver. With a vice-like grip, she cupped her tentacles and captured the prize. Her leg pivoted and deposited the object at the feet of Felipe. "See if you can do that Felipe!"

Felipe made three feeble attempts and then gave up. "It's just not fair, Florencia! Your feet are huge! You can kick better, jump higher, and run faster. Look! Stand next to me." With that, they stood up and sank their feet into the deep, warm sand. Both jumped back and viewed the marks in the sand that justified Felipe's assertion.

They raced back to the field of play.
Only in this field, danger was playing its own game of hide-and-seek.

Chapter 4

Don't Be a Cowboy

There's a wealth of amputation in the ground,
But no one can remember, where they put it down.

~Bruce Cockburn

While the children in Macachula avoided any sign of danger, Aderito Ismael went looking for it. Every day the scattered villages of Mozambique provided this Handicapped International leader with more than enough danger for him and his team of deminers.

Aderito's rugged off-road utility vehicle served as the daily command center. He pored over the tattered map spread across the entire hood. He gave the impression of an ex-commander of a special forces team, or a mercenary, or perhaps a game hunter. The sun was burning off the morning dew. Aderito's once breathable shirt was now clogged and the fragrance of each man's deodorant had evaporated in the first two hours of the day.

He removed the flat carpenter's pencil from his ear. He struggled to draw a clean line. He flicked the fallen drops off the surface of the map. Two solid circles appeared with black 'X's' marking various locations. The pencil returned to its former home.

Several team members gathered at the front of the vehicle to receive their assignments for the day. Had they not been so focused on the map they might have noticed the white bird flying directly overhead. None of them would have ever dared take their eyes off Aderito Ismael and the circles on the map.

"Remember, guys. What we're looking for is the size of a saucer in the ground. It won't put its hand up and say, "I'm here!"

Aderito finished the detailed instructions with his usual words; words that each man knew so well, that never failed to produce an ironic roll of the eyes from some of his comrades. Today would be no different.

"If a day comes and you realize you are cowboy enough to not be afraid of mines, please resign. Then you will not kill yourself and the others around you."

When the meeting was over Aderito folded the map and double-checked the graphite pencil was home, safe.

Not too many people rush to sign up for demining as an occupation. Aderito Ismael came to the hazardous work from a fascinating background. He was born into a family of eight in the small town of Luabo, Mozambique. Aderito was also born into a time of war.

In 1964, after 466 years under the rule of Portugal, the nation of Mozambique flexed its muscles and began a violent civil war in the cities and villages. The Portuguese military were thrown into a state of confusion and disarray by the guerilla tactics of the Russian-supported Frelimo forces. Mozambique was becoming the equivalent of Vietnam for the colonial army of Portugal. By the time Aderito de Jesus Ismael was born, in February 1967, they were three years into the decade-long War.

Luabo is a small town in the Zambezi region that, for many years, punched above its weight. The longstanding, British owned, sugar factory supplied the town and the region with employment and necessary transportation, with one of the main railways in Mozambique taking goods into Beira for export. Malawi borders the Zambezi region in the east and this valley saw a massive migration of a far different kind – refugees escaping the violence of an atrocity-filled war.

Aderito's father had been a medic in the army, and it became natural for him to train to become a nurse. In fact, had Aderito not been recently born, Aderito's father would have gone to Britain to train as a doctor. When Aderito was four years old his father changed occupation, from a nurse to a truck driver. His mother worked in the rice fields. A chance to start his own business, and the financial possibilities, was, honestly, too good to pass up. The Ismael family moved to the capital of the region, Quelimane, on the eastern coast of Mozambique.

Aderito's father hired a number of workers to serve his developing business. In the midst of colonial values where servants had little dealings with the members of a household, Mr. Ismael was a man altogether different. When one of his staff contracted a serious case of malaria, Mr. Ismael carried him in his arms to the hospital. The look on the faces of the doctors, nurses and other patients was of absolute surprise, if not disdain. For the owner of a company to show such compassion and go to such lengths was extraordinary. According to Aderito this typified the way his father lived, a truck driver with a nurse's heart. The story had an astonishing sequel. A few years later Aderito was busy driving through a village when he saw a man he recognized. Without any hesitation, he ran right up to the man and hugged him. Those around were astonished that a man of Aderito's stature could do such a thing. It was the man his father had carried into the hospital. Aderito greeted him like one of the family, which, in a way he was.

In the lottery of life, youths' dreams wither in the light of life's realities. Maybe the legs are not quite fast enough, or the skills not quite good enough. Perhaps the demand of a family's situation puts the dream on hold. It may endure for a decade, but one day the dream is cremated and the ashes are scattered like leaves in the fall. With the passage of time, the impossibility arrives. In the odd moment, here and there, forlorn and familiar words are found in the dictionary inside the mind and easily find their way to the tongue, *could have, should have, or might have.* The healthy ones, who are not the next Ronaldo, learn to enjoy the local team, or a kick around with their children. To these whole ones, there is still the fun of the game. Bad luck also plays a part in the game of destiny. It could be a car accident or an injury that puts an end to any possible career in sport.

Aderito Ismael was a fine sportsman. Unfortunately, he sustained a knee injury that still, to this day, plagues him. He did find some pleasure in turning to basketball from soccer and found some success, but the limits on travel and the state of the civil war curtailed longer term development in most sports. Another 'what might have been,' scenario. War and injury stopped a dream almost before it could begin. Aderito was fit enough for the army and joined up. Like many young men, Aderito Ismael discovered a conflict involving Mozambicans fighting Mozambicans strange and confusing. It was with profound relief that he completed three years and returned home.

Home had changed. Brothers and sisters had moved on and moved away to get on with the next phase of their lives. Aderito, now 22, was not the same person who had left three years earlier. War can accelerate or stunt personal growth. One thing is certain, life, as he had known it, was over. The aftermath of a civil war has a numbing effect. In a very real sense, there are no heroes in a civil war. There is an element of relief but not too many victory parades. The intensity of joy is muted. It would be a long road to recovery. For Aderito, there was no red carpet rolled out. No, what greeted him shocked him to his very core.

One evening, after dark, the Ismael family home had a visitor. Fortunately, the family was not home. The unwelcome, uninvited, guest was the war. A group of rebels, more like disorganized vandals, went on a rampage.

By the end of the night the family investments; trucks; farming properties; the machinery; a shop; and a bakery; were gone. Twenty years of hard work, scrapping and saving were burned to the ground in a few hours. Aderito's father tried to reach the place to evaluate the damage or at least recover whatever was left. The truck he was driving to get back was caught in an ambush.

A heavy air of poignancy and sadness is detected in Aderito's memory of the 'new normal.' Yet, here too, there is also a hint of a strong family trait – determined resiliency.

'Between my brother and myself we had to reach an agreement for one of us to work and the other follow his study. I chose to stay with my parents and take care of everything. My parents had lost some of the usual happiness we used to find in them. Their life sounded so very hard. There were, however, some noisy distractions. It was the younger ones who were left with them. Our parents couldn't escape sharing the low moments of their life with well-known icons such as Bruce Springsteen and Pink Floyd. For me, personally, with so many things happening and so much upheaval in my life, any dedication to my sports, simply, vanished.'

After the loss of everything, the Ismael lives became complicated and difficult. Aderito had to share the same school bag with his sister, for almost a year. Really, one schoolbag between two people, who were no longer kids! Yet, even this frustrating daily grind yielded a silver lining. Aderito's sister, Juleca, had to walk home every evening to give Aderito the bag, then he would return. A beautiful, intelligent and engaging young friend, Victoria do Carmo Papadakis would often accompany her on the walk. Aderito began to notice Victoria and the 'inconvenience' turned out to be the highlight of his day. Soon, conversation was flowing between Aderito and Victoria. Friendship blossomed into love. Out of the winter of discontent there was, now, a spring in each step – a walk of hope for a brighter future, together.

Aderito is a man who possesses a rare combination of strategic skills and a compassion for people. He was an obvious choice to work for

Save the Children and the United Nations Refugee Repatriation Service in 1992. The task was mammoth – to reunite families who had been displaced during the war. Some days could be soul destroying, spent in endless hours of interviews, inquiries, and dead ends. Some literally, the discovery of family members killed in the war. Then there were the other days – of unforgettable reunions of children with parents. The sheer joy on a little child's face, and a parent overcome and speechless with relief, was worth more than money could buy, or the salary earned. For the most part, Aderito was doing the graft of preparation and paving the way. Just occasionally, he also saw the fruit of his work and the actual reunion.

The work brought a variety of opportunities to show his ingenuity and command of unexpected situations. Off his own bat, Aderito went to a hospital and took basic training in delivering a baby. One had to be prepared for anything. Just as well he did. Aderito ensured any pregnant refugee traveled with him and not in the other vehicles. Labor happens, and happens anywhere. On two occasions, while crossing the border, the tell-tale signs of an impending birth turned his vehicle into a delivery suite. With no help around, and no other option, Aderito became the midwife in charge. He was calm and followed the procedures he had memorized. All went smoothly for both expectant mothers. In a nation where so many births are hazardous experiences, it was satisfying that mother and baby were in good health, albeit on a dark road in the bush, far from home.

He learned, long ago, to respect the bush, much like a marathon runner who respects the 26.2 miles. Not to do so, can be dangerous. Runners can be moving effortlessly at mile 19 and 'hit the wall' by mile 22. In an instant they can be staggering all over the road, like a town drunk, legs gone, and the mind too. Living may be simple in the bush, but nothing can be taken for granted: water, food, rain, safety. Since the days of the civil war, the ground has not been seen as a friend to grow crops and fruit trees, but as a lethal enemy to life and limb.

After almost three years with HALO, where he had begun his demining career, he moved on to work with Handicap International. Handicap

International, which was one of the leading organizations involved in removing the landmines from Mozambique. Aderito moved up quickly through the ranks to become a strategic trainer of deminers all across the country. To Aderito, this work was personal. Time was short and failure was not an option. His countrymen were counting on him to find the Black Widows before they struck again.

They could be anywhere. But, he could not be everywhere.

Chapter 5

Stolen Innocence

There are some things that once you've lost, you never get back.
Innocence is one. Love is another. I guess Childhood is a third.

~John Marsden

Florencia Artur stepped out purposefully. Strolling along the sandy path, she made her way to school. Although only a school girl she had the walk of an African queen. Everyone took notice how she moved. She held her head high, and her back was perfect, almost as if her normal seat was a throne in a palace. She, instinctively, carried that air of royal confidence with a winsome smile to match. Yet, she had a coy shyness. In a way, this made her all the more endearing.

The only break in her demeanor was when anyone, with even the slightest sense of humor, mentioned something funny. Florencia was an absolute godsend to a would-be comedian – she would lose every last ounce of her normal self-restraint and regal dignity. She chuckled and giggled long and loud until it was that belly laughter that is almost agony. If school friends were around, the scene could turn into a raucous, cacophony of girls howling laughter, the way only young girls can.

Most of the time the walk to school was quite pleasant. However, in the rainy season it could mean sinking one's feet into sludge or encountering a flowing stream. Like much of Africa, Mozambique struggles to cope with extremes. When nature seems to turn off its tap, long and devastating droughts can occur, without any end in sight. When heaven turns the tap on again and blows a mighty wind across the Indian Ocean, Mozambique could be in serious danger. It can be catastrophic. Hut homes are washed away, hundreds of thousands rendered homeless overnight, crops destroyed, animals drowned. For many, evacuation is the only possibility of survival.

In 2009, the village of Macachula had not suffered floods like Beira and Pemba to the north. But, it did experience a severe drought for two rainy seasons. The fields that normally produced crops were parched and barren. Maize doesn't grow too well when planted in cement. Food of any description was either scarce or very expensive. It's hard to make it on a wage of $1.25 per day. Throw in two years of drought and things get desperate.

As a young girl living a rural village in Mozambique, life is simple and peaceful. Yet, there is still much to be done: water to be fetched; firewood to be collected; pots to be cleaned; land to be tilled; laundry to be done (by hand); maize to be ground; cassava to be prepared and cashews shelled; and, the never-ending task of sweeping the hut. Florencia may walk like a queen, but, she can do the work of a man. Her strong arms and powerful legs can rise to any challenge. If Florencia did not carry herself with such charm and poise, one might exclaim, 'she's as strong as an ox!' In terms of strength, the description would not be too inaccurate. In terms of beauty, now that's an entirely different story - no offense to the ox.

The searing heat and stifling humidity sap the energy as they go about daily life. Yet, these women of Africa still find time and energy to try to sell surplus fruit and vegetables, clothes, or painted and polished shells.

Children sit and play quietly under the shade of a tree. As in many villages, men in Macachula are vastly outnumbered by the women. Some men find a job in another village. A few find their way, illegally, to South Africa and may never return to their home country. Then, there are the 'missing' men who have fallen prey to that most pernicious killer, HIV/AIDS. It is not uncommon for a mother to suffer the same fate. To read statistics on AIDS in London or Los Angeles is one thing – to touch the deep sadness of the human tragedies played out, is quite another. This is the mind-numbing narrative of Sub-Saharan Africa in the last thirty years.

Growing up in Mozambique is hazardous. For a young girl in this culture, it can be dangerous. Only eleven percent of girls go beyond elementary school. To put these facts in context, in a school of 2,000 pupils in the United States or the United Kingdom with 1,000 boys and 1,000 girls, 890 girls would be absent from school, never to return. We may ask, why? In many cases a father has died of HIV/AIDS, or a mother needs the help of her children, or the school is located at too great of a distance, or in the case of high school, the cost is too great. However, in Mozambique there are unique factors that prohibit young girls from completing their education. A key one is child brides.

The names and details may change in each village, but they tell strikingly similar stories. One in five girls is married by the age of fifteen. More than one-half are married by the age of eighteen – the seventh highest rate of child marriage in the world. While cultural rites of passage are prevalent in the north, the south of the country is known for 'child brides,' and a high incidence of adolescent pregnancies. At the core is an age-old belief system that girls and women are somehow inferior to boys and men. Some elements that contribute towards the continuation of child marriage are poverty, cultural practices and financial insecurity. The impact on these young girls cannot be overestimated.

Girls who marry before the age of eighteen are at a much greater risk of contracting HIV/AIDS and experiencing domestic violence. They are also less likely to be educated and receive economic opportunities. A mere one percent of female students enter college. This perpetuates the downward spiral of generational poverty. Once again we remind ourselves that these figures represent true stories of lives damaged and futures destroyed. A pregnancy in these teenage years can be physically dangerous, especially without proper care – rarely available in these villages. Pregnancy may be simple, but the birth may result in long term harm to the child's body. And the cultural shame attached can lead to the girl being married off young or sent away from her home. One thing is for sure, innocence has been lost forever.

Little did Florencia know just what lay ahead for her in the quiet village of Macachula.

A married man and father of four children took advantage of Florencia when she was still a young, shy, fifteen-year-old. She became pregnant. The man never came back to speak with her or offer any assistance. Alone, living with her mother, she dropped out of school. There was no alternative, and it was likely to be permanent. Another chance of an education was gone. Florencia's strength, both physical and mental enabled her to handle the pregnancy with fortitude. When she looked down at the most beautiful eyes and perfectly formed body of baby Guildo, suddenly the future brightened. New life ushered in a sense of joy and purpose. Her tiny baby was depending on Florencia. As her body recovered, she quickly returned to the routine responsibilities required to sustain their family. Guilda, Florencia's mother, would take care of Guildo.

One chair in a classroom sat empty. The little flower was missing. Florencia handled the laundry like a baker kneads the dough. Her fists squeezed the never ending supply of dirty sand out of each garment. School was out of the question for her, and she knew it. She had no time to dwell on the past, too many clothes to wash and vegetables to slice. School and the possibilities were escorted out of her imagination. Florencia was very good at adapting to change, not that she had a choice. Some boys she knew were off pursuing their education. *Guildo needs me more than I need school,* she thought.

Florencia's mother, Guilda, was slim and lacked any hint of the muscular prowess of her daughter. A caring and kindly woman, she took great delight in Guildo. It had taken her a few months to come to terms with yet another village girl, and her little flower, Florencia, losing her future to a wolf-like male. 'Why do they abandon us! Have they no sense of responsibility?' But one glance of her daughter's joy, one hold of her grandson, cast off those negative thoughts in a moment. It was a pleasure to rock him every morning when Florencia went off to collect the firewood for her daily cooking.

That particular day was a typical day in Macachula, light clouds, sunny and warm. Some of the villagers had been waiting for the rains to water the maize and cassava that they had planted. With the drought over they could look forward to a crop this year, and food of their own to cook.

Florencia was just starting to get into the rhythm of motherhood and getting a few more hours of sleep. Her mother noticed how much this mother adored and loved her son. The pain and the losses were already fading with each passing day. Florencia enjoyed bright colors, changing her hair style and, for a village girl, she always thought she was as trendy as any of the city girls she had heard about. She wouldn't have known the word trendy but she definitely modeled it. The best-dressed firewood collector in Mozambique.

The damp earth showed the imprints of her feet as she meandered along the well-worn path. The moisture of the soil moved between her toes and she felt a familiar tickle. Florencia glanced back at the foot imprint and immediately brought to mind the many times she and Felipe had measured their feet side by side. Maybe it was the feeling in her feet or the memory of Felipe – she grinned.

The wet firewood was not suitable. She began to look further afield for some 'dry' candidates. Returning home without firewood was not an option. With no wood, there would be no dinner. Florencia was standing by a couple of cashew trees. In one complete action, an outstretched arm reached up and she pulled down a couple of cashew nuts from a tree. They were popped into the small pocket of her blouse. She smiled and thought to herself, hmm...hmm, oh yes, this green blouse does go so well with my multicolored capulana.

The path was downhill for much of the way. At about half way the ground ascended up to a headland. The hilltop gave the adventurous a grand view of the land and the inviting turquoise ocean. Florencia spotted a couple of dry pieces of kindling off the path and under a bush. In the old, civil war, days the brow had been dangerous, but everything was clear now, thank God.

She did grab one good sized stick. Yes, it was bone dry. Another prospect lay just two or three steps away. Well, it might have been when Florencia was much younger. She took one of her famous giant strides and made a motion to swoop and pick it up. Florencia's strong, muscular right leg could cover the distance easily.

She was so quick she didn't even hear the click. BOOM!

The sudden, explosion was over in milliseconds... The eruption of gray smoke ascended to the sky.

Florencia's muscular body was tossed into the air and smashed to the ground like a rag doll. The lower part of her body was shredded and shrapnel 'spears' pierced the flesh to pieces.

Burning...Bloody...gnarled flesh smoldering like a log on a fire. A sulfur-like odor filled the air.

Surrounded by a sea of red, Florencia's immediate scream turned into loud moaning and groaning. Guilda instantly knew something tragic had happened to Florencia. She dashed out of her hut and ran toward the sounds of pain. As she got nearer Guilda saw the sight no mother ever wants to see, with cries of agony she never wants to hear. She fought back the tears that threatened to be a waterfall.

Guilda ripped off her capulana and immediately wrapped it around what was left of Florencia's right leg, which was hanging on by a few strands of tendon, almost miraculously. Blood was everywhere. By now a crowd of shocked and horrified neighbors had gathered. One person ran like an Olympian to get a truck. Within minutes a flatbed truck appeared and a group of men placed Florencia on the bed of the truck. Guilda was beside her. They set off on the tortuous journey over the undulating sandy excuse for a road. It would take almost two hours get to the tarmac road and then another two hours to a clinic. Florencia was losing more blood and barely conscious at times. Only the frequent bumps in the road jostled her and she managed to open her eyes. But her pulse and breathing were getting weaker and weaker by the kilometer. The groans were a dying whisper as life faded and heaven waited.

PMN 311-1 had waited twenty-seven years. The civil war had returned when nobody was 'at war.' It had come back with a vengeance. Nikolai had done his work, perfectly. Not that it mattered to him. He would never know.

PMN 311-1 had won its macabre game of hide-and-seek. Only this was no game. It was a real callous, senseless, act of heinous savagery. It crushed to the ground a beautiful, young flower and destroyed her life. It had taken a daughter from a mother, a mother from a baby son, and a human being with a name, Florencia.

The unsuspecting one.

The unfortunate one.

The unlucky one.

A flower in Africa had fallen.

Chapter 6

A Broken Flower

...A flower broken, folded over and downright thrown away.

~Earl Clifton

Those last fifty-eight kilometers to Macachula, Mozambique are difficult in the daylight and downright impossible at night. Fortunately, for Katya Cengel, the Toyota SUV pulled into the village with the sun high in the African sky.

"That's her house over there," said her driver as he passed by four 'homes' with similar architecture. The translator's finger pointed toward a hut made of sticks, mud and a thatched roof. Katya heard the words but was engrossed in the questions that were bombarding her mind. "How do people make a living here? Where's the school? Where do they get water? Where do they shop?"

The American journalist returned from her mental safari and she had two immediate thoughts. The first was in response to the declaration, 'that's her house over there!' Katya instantly recalled the children's story of the three pigs and the wolf, 'I'll huff and I'll puff and I'll blow the house down." This house would only need one puff, and a gentle one at that. In fact, if the weather turns real ugly and a cyclone sweeps in from the Indian Ocean, the thousands of huts are simply flushed away like waste in a sewage pipes.

The subsequent thought was the one that dominated Katya's mind. As if the journey to this remote village had not been tough enough to navigate, she now faced the most difficult part of this assignment; an interview that would involve three people, two languages, and one tragic accident.

The driver did his best to prepare the African woman for the interview with the reporter. In broken English he introduced Katya to Guilda and the three of them sat on a woven mat.

Guilda looked apprehensive, to say the least.

Katya Cengel is a seasoned professional and this was going to take every ounce of skill and sensitivity to pull it off. She sat down and took out her pad and pen – Guilda's eyes opened a little wider.

"Were you in your house when it happened?" Guilda nodded in the affirmative but concern was etched all over her face.

"Who was with you in your house?" Katya gently inquired, taking on an almost hesitant manner.

The words came ever so slowly like a painfully shy child. "Florencia's baby and my mother."

Katya moved closer and leaned in spoke quietly, but clearly, enough for the driver to translate.

"Guilda, I know that this must be terribly difficult, but can you tell me what you remember of that day?"

While the interpreter repeated the English to Katya to ensure its accuracy, Guilda shifted her position like a child when asked a question in class or a patient sitting in a dentist's waiting room.

Katya quickly marshaled her own inward caution with a calm, assuring, professional smile.

There was no such smile on the translator's face. His instinct told him to brace himself for a tense encounter.

Guilda looked down at the sand and the silence spoke volumes. A solitary tear trickled down her cheek. She muttered some unintelligible words, at least to Katya. It was all too obvious that the translator understood, perfectly. His eyes watered as he began to form the words.

"All I saw was a sea of red. All I saw was a sea of red…a sea of red." Katya took a deep breath. She chose not to speak. They waited.

After what seemed like a millennium the woman wiped her tear-stained face with her capulana.

Katya said. "How did you know it was Florencia?"

"Every mother knows her own child's cry. I knew. I knew…the groaning…the moaning…" Whatever she was going to say was lost in a heaving tsunami of emotion.

Some memories are too painful to share. The emotions are still too recent and raw.

"Would you like some water?" Katya ventured.

The small woman recognized Katya's obvious empathy and her face indicated genuine appreciation, despite the language barrier and the content of the conversation. Guilda continued with a flow of words that underlined a growing ease with this stranger. Katya began to connect with the courage of this little 'giant' who fought through the tears to describe the drama of the day.

"I ran as fast as I could. As soon as I saw Florencia, I thought she was going to die. How can you lose that much blood and live?

"When you're a mother, a strange power just takes over. I stripped off my capulana and wrapped it tightly, it was a bloody mess, like she'd been attacked by a lion. All the time I was shouting "Help! Please help me!" I didn't notice the sound of a truck arriving. Friends lifted Florencia and placed her on the metal bed of the green truck.

Katya was trying to get the story down yet maintain eye contact with Guilda.

"We left Guildo with my mother. I was with Florencia in the bed of the truck. To get to the clinic it takes four hours and the dirt road is bad. It was the worst journey of my life, but I knew I needed to be strong…strong for Florencia. Blood was still oozing from the leg and her arms and the other leg were charred. My mind was full of craziness. *Sixteen is too young to die. No mother should bury her daughter. Guildo needs his mother, not a grandmother. Why my Florencia?* "

This wasn't supposed to happen. I had to send my feelings to prison, if I didn't there would be no hope for my little flower. I thought, *we have been through so much in her short life. We have come too far for it to end like this.* So I repeated over and over, 'You're going to live, you not going to die, you can make it.' But she had the look of a fallen soldier about to die. "Guilda caught her rapid breathing and exhaled one of those deep as a cavern sighs, with an equally deep groan from the basement of her soul.

Guilda wiped her brow and blew her nose, and then resumed the story without any prompt from Katya. This wasn't the kind story that one listens to, you feel these stories. There was a lot of feeling in the Macachula air that afternoon.

"A lot of the time Florencia was drifting in and out, she was getting weaker and weaker. The blood never stopped. I kept talking, praying, talking and praying. But her life was ebbing away like the ocean tide retreating from the beach. I tried to hope for the best, but, inwardly, I feared the worst. Although every kilometer brought us closer to the clinic, it also brought Florencia nearer and nearer to death. "

It was a race against time, and there was a lot more road than time…

Part 2

CHANCE ENCOUNTERS

Chapter 7

Out of Adversity

Great moments are borne out of great opportunities.

~Herb Brooks in Miracle On Ice

The years following their trip to Mozambique had not been overly kind to John Mullen and Douglas Bowman. At least if one were looking through the lenses of dreams and hopes. Of course, there had been high-lights, many times of joy and laughter. Occasions of family successes were certainly celebrated but, honestly, they did not have quite the zest and spontaneity that characterized those of earlier days.

It is hard to throw yourself onto the dance floor with abandonment when there is the heavy weight of uncertainty of health or finances. Yes, we rise and transcend for the afternoon or the evening, but we do not leap out of bed to the 'dawn's early light' with a *carpe diem* attitude. More like the day seizes us than we seize the day.

There are a few relationships that defy years of separation and a multitude of personality differences.

That first fire of connection and friendship stands at the ready for immediate renewal at any moment. Decades can pass without much contact, yet, when the winds and events of life conspire and paths cross again, instantly the power of that unmistakable bond comes alive. The lost years vanish, tossed aside as irrelevant or meaningless compared to this fresh gift of a renewed friendship.

The magical or spiritual encounter that established a lifetime friendship—charged with energy and emotion – can be resurrected at any moment. Details have been stored in the hard drive of the mind. Emotions installed deep in the software of the soul, ready to be randomly accessed. Special memories and bonds from long ago. Possible to forget, but impossible to erase.

The habit of the intentional recall of the good and the pleasant of our past is a discipline that protects us in the dark and difficult seasons of life. To savor and taste again an extraordinary accomplishment or the achievement of another produces an active gratitude. If we allow this to percolate it can have a profound effect on the 'now' of our life. Instead of drinking the Kool-Aid and other potions that dull our senses to the current confusion or depression, we light up the shadows of the night of life with memories of the delightful and the beautiful. They stand as beacons of light when it's hard to see the way ahead and the temptation to despair is great.

In the places that matter in our minds, we are either laying landmines of negativity or building lighthouses of hope. For those who think this is easy, they are mistaken. It is not. It is very difficult. For those who think it is complicated, they are wrong too. It is not. It is simple.

Though radically different in so many ways, John and Douglas do have a common trait – they are risk takers, holy gamblers if you will. Not quite in the same areas or in the same manner, but they are both willing to live close to the territory of Kipling's advice in his poem 'If,'

If you can make one heap of all your winnings
And risk it on one turn of pitch-and-toss,
And lose, and start again at your beginnings
And never breathe a word about your loss;
If you can force your heart and nerve and sinew
To serve your turn long after they are gone,
And so hold on when there is nothing in you
Except the Will which says to them: 'Hold on!'

The 'long-lost-friends-meet-again-moment' happened outside the Hoffmann Brat Haus restaurant at the Paseo Nuevo Mall in Santa Barbara in February of 2015. It was to prove as decisive as that day on the soccer field at Santa Ynez some fifteen years earlier. Since then John had tried several entrepreneurial exploits that had not quite worked out. Like so many businesses around the nation John's real estate development company had run right, smack-bang into the 2008 headwinds of the recession. He might say the Great Recession. Well, great meaning giant or monstrous. In the ensuing years, he had never quite recovered from the devastating effects of this global downturn. It proved a death blow to so many. Health challenges provided yet more opportunities to live in stress rather than peace. Staying positive is both a daily work and a daily grace.

Douglas and the love of his life, Fiona, had met with several disappointments of their own. They had explored, unsuccessfully, the possibility of Fiona nursing overseas. The only thing to materialize was being stuck in a near civil war after a contentious election in Kenya. There were days that only Dickens words were appropriate…

'They were the best of times and the worst of times.'

The Bowmans were working in New Zealand, thousands of miles away from Scotland, when Fiona's mother passed away. Douglas could not travel to the funeral. He had a life-threatening blood clot millimeters from his femoral artery. At the same time, their daughter Laura was struggling with health issues in Boston. Frankly, from one point of view, life sucked. Yet, it was a time where they made friends with neighbors and a marvelous group of people from a host of countries from around the globe. In   this emotionally challenging period for Douglas and Fiona, so many of those friends went out of their way to love. How often kindness fed and empathy lent an ear? No sooner had she recovered than Laura ran in the ill-fated Boston Marathon on the devastating Patriot's Day. She was running along Commonwealth Avenue just a couple of minutes from the Boylston Street finishing line. She had actually been scheduled to cross the line at the time the first of the two bombs exploded. It would be three horrendous hours in Queenstown, New Zealand before Douglas and Fiona heard Laura's shaken voice. Tears of relief flowed.

Queenstown was a trial and a joy. Just when they didn't know what would befall them next, Fiona literally did, fall that is. The home in which they lived had loads of natural light, courtesy of some very high windows and skylights. Fiona, on her high perch, was busy wiping the last smudges away when the extra tall ladders decided to do a gymnastic move, the splits. Despite valiantly grabbing for the curtain rail she dropped to the wooden floor. She shattered her heel. Two doctors said it was quite possible that she may not walk again, certainly not with any degree of ease, or on any difficult terrain. As with so many occasional crises in their lives, Fiona defied the odds, but the healing process was painful, painstaking, and lengthy. Yet again a few friends in Queenstown went the extra mile, and then some, in demonstrating their friendship in a myriad of practical expressions. They were then, and are now, the salt of the earth.

So, when Douglas arrived in Santa Barbara in time for Thanksgiving in 2014, there seemed little for which to be grateful, at least if one concentrated on the current debit column in the balance sheet of life's experience. Fiona had applied for, and accepted, a nursing job in Mammoth, California. Douglas was pleased for her – nursing had always been more than a mere job for Fiona. For her, it was a vocation. We are always happier when we follow our calling. Whatever the future, the present was uncertain, and the inner legacy of the wounds of love, so daily. Anyone who has been through this kind of season can echo, only too well, the words of Shakespeare in Hamlet,

'When sorrows come,
they come not in single spies
but in battalions....'

John and Douglas began to take early morning walks along the famed Santa Barbara waterfront. It was a time to cast their fishing line into the ocean of history and hook some miracles that they had seen in Mozambique; the blind saw; the deaf heard; the dumb spoke and the poor received food and good news.

A phrase that they had heard time and time again was, 'Stop for the One.' What was so unusual was that the group of people that they were with actually put these words into action. They stopped for the orphan, the elderly, the sick, the lost, the widow, the depressed, and the lame. This was a depth of outrageous, continuous compassion on such a level of authenticity not seen before by neither John nor Douglas. It was like a missile, targeted straight at the mediocrity and malaise of their lives. It didn't miss.

There were strange phenomena that occurred on their once-in-a-lifetime trip, things that were hard to explain. Some could make you laugh. Most made you weep. But, for both of them, it was as if Jesus himself had just stepped out of Nazareth into Mozambique and started doing his stuff, again. Back in Santa Barbara, church was normal, nothing 'strange' ever happened – no blind people saw, no lame walked, well none that they knew of. But, when you have seen this with your own naked eye, it produces a conviction that something is far adrift these days with faith in America and the West. All of this swirled around their minds as they walked every morning in Paradise. They had seen those in Mozambique with nothing, who nonetheless were happier and more content. These who seemed crazy apparently had the attention of Someone Greater than themselves. More than anything, John answered their requests. John and Douglas answered their requests and more than anything fell in love with Mozambique and her people. Frequently, their morning stroll was punctuated by sighs, with each memorable incident that came to mind.

It is interesting to note that men like Steve Jobs and other significant business guys began to promote walking as a means of problem solving and creating solutions to various issues. Looking straight into another panorama of beauty, the early morning sunrise over the beach in Santa Barbara, John and Douglas sensed an urge and a responsibility to record the experiences of those heady days in Mozambique.

On a walk at dawn, John casually said, "We should write a book."

They knew, instinctively, this moment was one of those rare instances that a few people have in their lifetime. Some have too much noise going on in their world and don't hear the whisper. Others hear, but the thought dies on the barren ground of their low self-esteem or is suffocated under the avalanche of their fears. Still others rationalize that they have too many problems or situations to face. But some know that they must put everything to one side, and, just do it. Little did John and Douglas know what lay in store once they both spoke an inner 'yes' to this literary call from the Great Author. Despite the adversity of their mutual situations, or maybe because of them, they decided they should make a start. They did, the next morning.

On the white board, fifteen chapters were mapped out.

All went exceedingly well. Not only was the project moving swiftly, it was fun. At the outset, both agreed on one key element. They would trust their gut instinct on what to write, and they would try to recapture the 'feel' of those days in Mozambique. One morning, with ten chapters of the book completed, a game-changing thought popped up. It was out of the blue. 'Not many people have much of a clue about the country of Mozambique, its size, location, or the problems it has faced and is facing.' The fact is many people couldn't even pin the country on a map of Africa. Some might even put it in the Pacific Ocean.

In a brain dump, many ideas came to mind. Economics, politics, a more detailed geography, education, and social factors. Douglas began to yawn. While all of these were possible, none seemed to highlight the kind of human interest story that would capture their reader's attention.

After much discussion three areas rose to the top of the whiteboard; cyclones, poverty, and............... landmines.

The last word caused the hair on the back of John's head to stand at attention. He repeated it in a hushed whisper, "landmines."

Chapter 8

Sowing the Seed

No matter what people tell you,
words and ideas can change the world.

~Robin Williams

*L*andmines... Douglas clapped his hands with delight. He, instantly, recalled the road to Beira. It was like he'd scored a goal on the soccer field. For him, the trip to Beira had been the disappointment of an adventure missed. But, the tinge of sadness only lasted a few seconds. That was how long it took for him to realize the research would throw up a memory or two for John. *'Ha, perhaps, even a rewriting of the Beira nightmare.'* Douglas entertained, for a moment, a morbid sense of devilish delight. For some reason- John did not seek the reason for Douglas's mirth. He did not need to ask.

Both of the authors set about researching data and stories related to landmines, how they worked and where were they manufactured, and, importantly, how did they affect Mozambique. Douglas unearthed a document by a writer in Chicago. In the article the details of the number of mines and the massive danger to life and limb were outlined. Also made clear was the economic impact on the nation that depended heavily on its agriculture.

Included in the article was a story about a young sixteen-year-old girl, Florencia Artur, who had stepped on a landmine in the bush of Mozambique. The short piece included a heart-wrenching photo of Florencia, with her right leg amputated above the knee and her left leg badly scarred from the burns caused by the landmine. It was the 'perfect' human interest incident. They merely needed to verify the details.

John and Douglas arranged for a conference call with Chris, the author of the article. They were concerned to verify the story and perhaps, if necessary, obtain permission to use it in their book. Chris was most accommodating; even though he was just days away from becoming a father for the first time. It is astonishing how often life changing events and movements that will influence so many people hinges on a fragile thought or a chance encounter. They concluded that they had enough information to craft a story about this poor, unfortunate, young woman in the middle of nowhere in Mozambique.

Over their morning latte, John cautioned Douglas in going down the *Three Cups of Tea* road, a book once lauded by readers and critics alike, which turned out to have many parts that were exaggerated. It would turn out to be another 'coffee-shed' moment. Douglas clicked on Google. He immediately recognized the purple headline indicating he had already read it. Just as he was about to click on the text and be taken to the story, his keen eye spotted a blue headline two or three results lower than Chris's. It was an article about women in Mozambique being hired and trained as deminers. In the extended synopsis a name stood out, Florencia Artur, but the age was different 17, not 16. That was odd.

Douglas read the whole *National Geographic* piece. True to the title the narrative described how these women who had been earning $1.25 per day were now earning $300 per month and it had transformed their lives. Tucked away in the article was the story of Florencia. It was 217 words, brief but poignant and powerful. Even the second reading of the incident had Douglas weeping. He read it aloud to his co-author and friend. John cried. Something unusual was taking place. Douglas returned to the article to find out the author's name. It was written by a Katya Cengel.

John looked up Katya's name on LinkedIn. In a delightful twist, the first of many that were to come, her profile revealed she was an adjunct lecturer of Journalism at California Polytechnic University, San Luis Obispo – just ninety miles north of Santa Barbara. A call with Katya was scheduled. Douglas told John that his mom would have called this 'predestined good fortune.' Others prefer stroke of luck. Either way, it was, unexpectedly, good news.

John and Douglas prepared some questions for their time with Katya. The day before the call they were thinking about Florencia and her plight and how to craft her story to do it justice. Maybe it was the word justice that triggered an exchange of ideas about how the story should be framed. They would create an awareness of the destruction wrought upon Florencia's life by these immoral landmines.

Within seconds it dawned on the two authors that 'stop for the one' did not mean 'write about the one.' It meant, *do* something for the one. Florencia needed a better ending to her story, and John and Douglas could certainly use a better ending to theirs. The seed of a quite outlandish, outrageous idea was planted in their minds. On the face of it, it was a ridiculous notion. Crazy – like Archimedes the Greek Mathematician making his discovery in the bath, shouting, "Eureka". *I found it.* He got so excited he forgot to put his clothes on when he ran out into the streets to tell the world of his discovery. These two writers didn't go naked into the streets, for which their nearest and dearest were extremely appreciative. Yet they were just as convinced and excited.

They would get Florencia a leg.

So a fresh question was placed at the top of the list of questions to ask Katya. *How can we get in touch with Florencia?* Katya turned out to be warm, articulate and with a degree of intrigue. After a few polite introductions

John and Douglas moved into the heart of the conversation with Katya. They inquired about how she came to be in Mozambique. Katya had been researching two or three topics as a sponsored journalist. She had heard of Florencia's tragic accident from some of the demining women. Katya recounted her 'adventure' traveling to the village of Macachula to meet with Florencia and her mother. Although she had moved on to pursue other human stories, her vivid memory of that day indicated a sincere interest in John and Douglas's story that was unfolding before their very eyes. Most of what happened was, thankfully, lost to Florencia. Guilda had filled in as much as she could. Katya sketched the few details she had gleaned and described them. As John and Douglas were glued to the iPhone in the center of the desk, the rest of the story was as captivating as it was gut wrenching.

The flower of Macachula somehow, miraculously, survived the harrowing journey. The flatbed made it to the clinic with Florencia alive. Tragically, Florencia's right leg had to be amputated, just above the knee. The left leg was badly scarred. She was in the clinic for two and half months. An old pair of crutches, barely suitable, and certainly not comfortable, became her lifeline to move, probably for rest of her life. Although overcome with shock and sadness at her new reality, Florencia was desperate to return to Macachula to hold little Guildo. By the time she arrived home to Macachula, she struggled to get out of the truck with one and one-half legs and two metal poles.

Guildo was fifteen months old. Months of separation can feel like years to a toddler and a heartbroken mother. Although thankful to be back, Florencia had to come to terms with a bleak road ahead. A road she had to take on make-shift props.

It was a good thing the call was not a Skype video call. Katya would have seen the frequent tears trickling down the faces of these two grown men. They composed themselves to ask Katya the question that was now preoccupying their every waking hour.

"Do you know how we can find her? We want to get her a prosthetic leg."

Katya's momentary incredulity at the very idea soon switched gears. She checked her contact list for one email address in particular. If there was any possibility at all that this most bizarre of missions could end in success, Katya had to find that email. She found it. Aderito de Jesus Ismael. "Guys, if there is any chance of helping Florencia you need this man. He speaks English, knows the area, and has many contacts. And, most importantly he's the kind of man who will stop at nothing. If it can be done, he will do it."

Aderito had originally been going to take Katya to Macachula. However, as a manager with Handicapped International handling the demining efforts he had been called away to an urgent meeting. He did make sure she was well looked after since the journey was somewhat difficult. Katya had not really kept up with him, other projects called for her attention and Aderito was one of those men who was always moving on to the next strategic plan or training. Katya agreed to email Aderito and make an introduction for John and Douglas. She would also mention the possibility they wanted to explore.

When John and Douglas concluded the conversation and thanked Katya, there were a few seconds before they both let out a, "Whoa, what did we just do?" Now, it wasn't so much a question of, if it was possible, they knew they must make an 'attempt.' Actually, on further reflection, the word attempt left room for failure. That day they decided that if Aderito would help them, they would not tolerate anything less than success– a young single mother walking again.

Douglas looked up the name Florencia – it means 'Flower.'

Florencia's stem might be broken, but this British pastor and American businessman would move heaven and any obstacle on earth to restore what the instrument from hell had taken away. In a spacious first floor office in Santa Barbara some virtues began to whisper. They whispered of qualities these writers would need. Compassion stirred even more in the heart, to feel deeply the loss of Florencia's dignity. Dignity called to Justice to do something. Justice summoned Courage to silence fears. Courage spoke to Determination, 'there are obstacles to be overcome. Douglas and John heard all the voices. The Archimedes rush had now passed and moved into a strong sense of purpose. This would become their all-consuming passion and focus, the one thing they would do.

There would be no peace, nor rest, until the Flower of Macachula stood up like a Princess again, and walked holding Guildo in her arms, or, hand in hand to collect firewood.

Between classes at Cal Poly University, Katya Cengel quickly wrote her introduction email to Aderito and pushed send:

> *Hello Aderito,*
>
> *I hope you have been well since I saw you last summer while reporting on the efforts of female deminers in Mozambique.*
>
> *I am writing to introduce you to John Mullen and Douglas Bowman, copied on this email. John and Douglas live in California but traveled to Mozambique previously and are interested in supplying landmine victims like Florencia Artur in Inhambane province with prosthetics. I was hoping you might be able to help them make this happen by connecting them with the right people and advising them on how they could get prosthetics to Florenicia and other landmine victims in Mozambique.*
>
> *I would love to hear how you are doing and any updates on the landmine situation in Mozambique.*
>
> *Best, Katya*

The email sat unopened in Aderito Ismael's mailbox.

In Inhambane, Aderito was busy shifting furniture, selling computers, erasing hard drives, and performing a multitude of tasks related to shutting down demining operations for Handicap International Mozambique. At the same time, he was stressed to the max, wondering what on earth he was going to do in the future. And the future was coming faster than an express train. He had spent almost two decades of his life as a technical expert in directing demining efforts across the country.

There were now two options; be unemployed in his own country, and pursue an entirely new career; or be exiled to another mine-laden nation,

Angola for example. The second option was one that he would only accept as a last resort. He had sacrificed so much time away from Victoria and the children, that the prospect of another lengthy sojourn was the last thing on his mind. The only upside to the second option was he would be paid well. The first option was equally challenging, but for different reasons. What could he do? He had formed a company with the idea of helping those who had been maimed by landmines. But he had little, or no capital to continue his venture. Perhaps, in the longer term, but that was not the answer to the current situation. A complete career change was not, exactly, thrilling him either. The thoughts kept coming, thick and fast, tossed around inside his head.

In those rare moments of quiet, when the day's work was over, he would allow himself to relax with a cold beer. Then he pondered the work that had been achieved by President Chissano, the man who empowered the transition from war torn Mozambique into a flagship of democracy in Africa. He established significant, financial growth despite natural disasters and the ensuing crises. President Chissano had once remarked it might take over one hundred years to remove all the mines from the land. Now, they were a few months away from the announcement, and the exciting newspaper headlines, that the country was, 'Mine Free.' The expense had been enormous, some estimates were as high as $250,000,000 dollars, given from countries around the world. It was completed in less than twenty years, despite the interruptions of floods and other disasters. The mammoth task had taken men, women, dogs, and, yes, giant rats to get the job done. Actually, the rats were some of the most efficient deminers.

Now, Aderito was in the middle of his final operation. He was rapidly moving around the country training police divisions for any 'situation' that might occur. These policemen could not have been in better hands than this demining MacGyver, who would leave nothing to chance.

When the future was not front and center in Aderito's thoughts and emotions, the events of the years would present themselves on the stage of his mind. He had felt this way before. When the work with Save the

Children had come to an end there was a satisfying sadness. He had seen, face to face, the joy of a family reunited after years apart. Yet there was a sense of loss for a noble, caring job coming to an end. The demining work had a different kind of satisfaction but, it was there nonetheless. The removal of these dastardly weapons of human destruction was vital. Nobody could calculate the number of children, young people, mothers and fathers who are alive today in Mozambique because of the magnificent work done by the demining teams. But once again, something of immense value was ending.

Nostalgia easily recalled the friendships, trials, obstacles overcome and the laughter of colleagues. Moving on is a necessary part of living, but the healthy ones allow themselves to pause, feel the grief, give thanks for the years, and then let go. Without that process, the change is often resisted rather than embraced. The result damages the new situation when it finally arrives. Genuine attempts by others to befriend are met with pleasantness, but no depth, and slowly a shell is produced to protect the soul from the potential pain of the future. The protected areas isolate even in a crowd, and the pulse the soul becomes weak. Hidden away, lurking in the recesses of his core, Aderito was detached, alone, and lost. Years on the road, doing marriage and family at a distance, had left him a stranger watching the children he loved grow up, all from a distance. *Just what will I do?* He asked himself. It was a recurring question.

In Aderito's line of work every day could be the last day on earth for somebody, or the last day someone walked on two legs. It is fraught with danger. The images in Aderito's mind played back familiar scenes. It was uncanny, like the events took place yesterday. He could see himself, on locations, smell the familiar sulfur of a controlled explosion, recognize the faces, name the names, recall a few disasters, and some near misses. He hadn't had too many cowboys, thankfully. Most of his teams were excellent. Even his fears that the recruitment of women to join the team could prove difficult had been totally unfounded. Indeed the women had brought an expertise and perspective which was invaluable. The idea of hiring women could have been a serious disruption, instead, it was a stroke of genius. He carefully placed the photos of his teams in a cardboard box. The photos and the memories were both locked away, dismissed and in the dark, much like Aderito himself. He wondered what these former colleagues were doing, if they had a job, if the women were back earning one dollar fifty per day - safe, but poor. If he didn't create something soon poverty would be knocking on his door. But, in this solitary, lonely space, he faced lot more than financial drought.

He grabbed the final plastic container of office supplies – his 'personal effects.' locked the door, and left.

He turned the key in the SUV and gave a quick glance at the sign in the office window.

For Lease.

Chapter 9

A Man For All Seasons

It is part of a good man to do great and noble deeds,
though he risks everything.

~Plutarch

Aderito Ismael was mortified. *How on earth did I miss this email? It's two weeks old!*

Others, knowing the stress surrounding Aderito's life, would have easily accommodated his oversight. His circumstances had become almost unbearable. A fire had partially damaged his own house and then spread next door to his neighbor's home, and burned it to the ground. His savings had been depleted rebuilding his neighbor's house. His personal vehicles were burned or broken down. His job of fifteen years had just ended. To say that life was uncertain would be an understatement. Like Douglas and John, Aderito's 'sorrow and troubles had come in battalions.' Adversity was everywhere.

His eyes darted back and forth reading Katya's email...…

Two men. Writers. Looking for Florencia. Get her a leg?

Florencia........ Florencia?

Ah! The girl who stepped on the landmine in Macachula!

A prosthetic?

Hardly any landmine victims get prosthetics in my country…

He hastily shot off an apologetic email to John Mullen.

June 1

Hello John

I'm really sorry for not responding earlier. Mozambique is approaching the end of demining operations, we stopped operations recently and demobilized the teams. I was preparing my archives and Katya's email. My contract with Handicap International was terminated at the end of April and I am still between things here. You can use the cell number below to call or Skype.

> *Thanx,*
> *Adérito Ismael*

The email didn't contain anything to warrant wild enthusiasm on the part of the two writers. Yet, by no means was it a dead end. The needle on the possibility meter had been stuck. It was now quivering. A Skype call was set up and, because of Aderito's compacted itinerary, it took a couple of weeks to put the call in place.

In the days while they waited for the Skype call from Aderito, John and Douglas read anything they could lay their hands on that related to landmines in Mozambique. Sifting through the statistics and papers threw up wildly exaggerated numbers, both in terms of the landmines laid, the cost of removing the mines, and the number of innocent victims that had suffered from, accidentally, stepping on a mine. Old propaganda from the various factions littered cyberspace. They decided to stick with the figures from the reports that were produced from the international conferences that had been held periodically, over the last few years. Some of those conferences had been hosted in Maputo, Mozambique.

In terms of anti-personnel landmines, one could not help noticing that over 129 countries had signed the treaty banning the barbaric tool of creative destruction, intended for pure acts of evil. Most were not designed to kill soldiers in a war but maim civilians and then exploit the breakdown of the enemy resources trying to deal with the 'situations.' The only absentees from that extensive list are Russia, China, USA, and Israel. These nations refuse to comply with the ban. The first three nations have been some of the major manufacturers of these devices. Of course, none have exploded on their lands, only in other nations to whom they have sold their 'products.' The reports did not make for easy reading. Douglas was surprised at the lack of voices being raised about Landmines. There were some, one being Princess Diana who had become quite the crusader to highlight the danger of the landmines to civilians and raise the profile of the victims around the world. In the course of the research, Douglas ran across a song, extraordinary in its lyrics. He wanted to know more about the singer and the songwriter. One man produced both melody and lyrics.

The disturbing and prophetic song was penned by Canadian activist Bruce Cockburn. Cockburn has been a man of practical faith. Only this brand of faith was truly biblical in character. Unlike what passes for faith in much of America and the West, this kind of belief refused any idea that justice and faith could be separated. That's a kind of spiritual apartheid that produces a consumerist 'selfie' Christianity on the one hand and little more than a political protest movement on the other. Cockburn's 'faith' got him into trouble with critics everywhere. Still, the one he was following had been no stranger to controversy. In fact, he was crucified with nails as well as words.

The faith community didn't like Cockburn messing with politics. It didn't matter to them that their ancient text, about which they were so proud that they 'believed every word of the inerrant book,' was quite clear that the people of faith are called to 'do justice.' The activists were disgusted with Cockburn's frequent mention of his allegiance to Christianity and its Founder. There was indeed a spiritual foundation that undergirded everything which Cockburn believed, and spoke. Cockburn wasn't about to be swayed by either camp. Back in the mid to late nineties, he was really stirred by the war torn, landmine laden landscape of Mozambique, and particularly the interference of other nations, doing all they could, intentionally or otherwise, to cripple this beautiful country, permanently. So, he penned some strong, descriptive, provocative, lyrics.

There's a wealth of amputation
Waiting in the ground
But no one can remember
Where they put it down
If you're the child that finds it there
You will rise upon the sound
Of the mines of Mozambique

Some men rob the passersby
For a bit of cash to spend
Some men rob whole countries dry
And still get called their friend
And under the feeding frenzy
There's a wound that will not mend
In the mines of Mozambique

The best estimate of amputees in Mozambique was reported in 2014. The government estimated this number between 8,000 to 12,000 with about 4,000 registered. The report was bleak. All the resources from the nations had gone into mine removal. There had been an attempt to help the victims in the years immediately after the civil war. But that stopped by 1996 and the severe poverty and devastating floods meant little or nothing had been done by way of wheelchairs or prosthetics. In addition, the victim list grew every year as the hidden Black Widows achieved their dastardly intentions. These innocent ones had been going about their normal life, walking to school, planting crops, fetching water, or wood for the fire. One moment humming a tune; the next instant, blown apart, or, even dead.

By now the 'tap on the shoulder' to write their own book had become a passionate quest for John and Douglas to find Florencia, and somehow, get her a leg. The sheer reality of around 10,000 others laying in the scattered villages of Mozambique, valiantly trying to pursue a semblance of normality, grabbed their attention, daily. There were many moments of weeping as pain-filled stories were found. Often the two writers would read them out loud. There is something in the voice that connects to our very souls. It pierces the walls that we strive to keep maintained, part of our protection system. It's like a wall around the heart and a mask over the face. It all adds up to a stoic unreality. When that wall comes down, fresh seed-sized possibilities are sown and there is an openness to others. We cease to rationalize why we can't change situations, the old arguments to defend inactivity for good falls like a line of dominoes. The imagination lights up and there is an awakened realization of what can be done for others.

Douglas and John could do nothing for those long since buried in the same soil that killed them. But, they had a sense of energy and focus for the ones who are still existing, but not living. They would, 'Stop for the One,' but there was now no way that they could stop at one. Every one of Florencia's ten thousand friends deserved compassion and the chance to walk again. Justice demanded it, and as one famous man, who knew a fair amount about injustice personally once put it, 'Injustice anywhere is Injustice everywhere.' It is one thing to recite it, it is quite another to feel it. It is one thing to feel strongly about injustice, but those who have suffered injustice do not need feelings. They need actions. Justice is not a speech, nor even a truth. It's an activity.

The Skype call came and a smiling Mozambican appeared on the screen of John's computer.

Following initial pleasantries on Skype, Aderito began to share his personal story and his compassion for the victims of landmines. While he had directed the extrication of the landmine immediately after the accident he had never met Florencia. She was still in the clinic when the demining took place. The only difficulty of any significance was the internet was not quite as good as our personal connection. Douglas and John were soon to discover that Aderito was even more doggedly persistent as they were. Then, some bad news. A prosthetic in Mozambique would cost in the region of $12,000 to $15,000 dollars. No wonder these $1.25 per day villagers had no hope of ever being fitted with a leg.

Aderito made John and Douglas aware that the journey was no walk in the park, or a ride in the country. In fact, it could be the drive from hell. He had advised every visitor to Macachula it was imperative to enter in the daylight and leave before dark. Even Aderito, with his Army service and years demining in many villages, would not attempt it at night. The sandy excuse for a road was uneven with exaggerated, furrows, and paths, undetectable and unmarked. There was no question, in Aderito's mind, that he would make the trip. Aderito was not so confident in the success of the overall venture. He thought the writers were, just a little short of, crazy. But, he countered, 'better at least try to do something for Florencia, than do nothing.'

Aderito created a gap in his schedule to make the trip. He informed John of the dates. The nursed gearbox failed on the way and needed more surgery. Timing the arrival for daylight also meant getting lodging for a night, on the way and on the return journey. Eventually, the determined Aderito made it to Macachula.

The first part of the mission was accomplished. Now to find Florencia.

Chapter 10

Finding a Hidden Treasure

A man discovered a hidden treasure in a field and
sold everything he owned and bought the field.

~Matthew 13:44

He found her hut and peered in. Nobody was there. He turned and off in the distance he saw Florencia approaching. She was unmistakable. Aderito knew she was the only amputee in her village. With the grace of a gymnast, she planted the rubber tips of the forearm crutches into the deep soft sand and shifted her weight forward. She then lifted her good leg and took a step while her crutches easily found the next suitable point of contact.

One of the crutches had a broken cuff which caused her arm to slip while she walked. This didn't hinder Florencia. Sixteen months earlier she had walked like a drunk sailor, often falling. But now, she was an expert in the art of movement with broken crutches. Strength, agility, and balance in perfect harmony. Aderito was impressed, even shocked at the speed at which she sped across the ground. She's moving faster than I can walk. As she drew closer, Aderito could see the 'good leg' was seriously damaged. Someone had previously described that leg on the day of the accident as a 'mass of gnarled flesh.' Although damaged, it was still strong and fortunately for Florencia, extremely effective.

Aderito greeted Florencia's mother Guilda, and her son Guildo. He reminded Guilda that he and his demining team had worked in Macachula to check for the existence of more mines after Florencia's accident. He explained that he had come on a very important mission and needed to speak with Florencia. Guilda went inside the hut and left Florencia and Guildo to sit on the bamboo mat outside.

Aderito pulled out a piece of paper. John and Douglas had composed a simple letter to Florencia. On his haunches, Aderito tried his best to tell Florencia of his unusual connection with Katya Cengel, and two men in California. Aderito read the letter slowly.

June 15, 2015

Florencia Artur Manhiça

Dear Florencia,

We want to formally introduce ourselves to you. We are Douglas Bowman and John Mullen, and we're from Santa Barbara, California in the USA. Our associate, Aderito Ismael has traveled from Maputo to bring you our greetings and speak with you about our desire to help you.

Both Douglas and I traveled to Mozambique in 2002 as part of a mission group where we helped feed and care for orphans and widows. We fell in love with your country and especially with the precious people of this nation.

We heard about your story through an article in National Geographic magazine. Katya Cengal, an independent writer, wrote this article in December of 2014 regarding the issue of landmines and the current demining operations. She also interviewed you and shared about your tragic accident and the many challenges you've faced as an amputee. We contacted Katya and Aderito, and they helped us to find you.

We are currently writing a book about our experiences in Mozambique. For both of us, this trip was life changing and it opened our eyes to the needs of so many that have been victims of the war and the devastating floods. We were aware of the demining operations when we visited, but we were not aware of the thousands of victims who have been maimed by detonated landmines. In our book, we will be addressing the plight of victims such as yourself. We don't just want to talk about this issue. We want to do something about it. Our goal is to help people like yourself to be fitted with prosthetics and to be able to have greater mobility, which will allow you to carry on normal activities like caring for your child, attending school and going to work.

It is our hope that you will let us help you. We believe that your story is important and the world needs to be aware of this need. Please let Aderito know if you would give us permission to measure you and have you fitted with an artificial leg. If this is acceptable to you, we would return and measure your leg on the next visit and then come back a third time to fit you with the prosthetic.

We look forward to talking to you and pray God's blessing on your life.

Sincerely,
John D. Mullen
Douglas Bowman
HOW International, Inc.

Aderito paused at key moments to check if Florencia understood. He wasn't sure. The most important detail he double checked. Did she understand that, with the help of a prosthetic, she could walk again? It took a little time but Florencia said yes, she would like to walk again. Florencia was shy and withdrawn. Aderito tried in vain to communicate with John and Douglas knowing they were eagerly awaiting news. He tried standing on top of his SUV with his computer. No luck.

Then he climbed a tree looking for a satellite signal. Nothing. The last rays of sunlight were fading and dusk was descending rapidly.

The indomitable Aderito tried one last time and managed a one minute call, gave John and Douglas the report, and told them, he really had to go, but would call when he was in a safe place with a better connection.

In an office in Santa Barbara, California, two men sat, each with moist eyes, smiling. There was no boyish excitement in the air. Far too much to do, and too many obstacles to face. Instead, there was enormous admiration for this Good Samaritan from Maputo. He had gone an extra seven hundred miles, and at a period in his life when he could have been excused for simply saying, 'it's just not possible at the moment.' Not Aderito. If Aderito Ismael says he is going to do something, he does it.

That late afternoon he drove through the blackness of night for the hazardous return journey. Two and a half days out of his life at the request of two men thousands of miles away. There were drips on the steering column, but not from sweat.

John and Douglas told Aderito that they would reimburse him for his considerable expenses. True to his character, when he could have really used some funds, Aderito turned down the offer. How rare. Goodness for goodness sake. It's the humanitarian way – the true philanthropy – love for mankind.

Philanthropy does come at a cost, financial and emotional.

It was that potential cost of philanthropy that was taking prime place in John and Douglas's office and lunchtime conversations. The mathematics of $15,000 dollars per leg. Whether the prosthetic is cheap or expensive the life of a single prosthetic leg is between 4 -7 years. Say an average of 8 legs for 10,000 landmine victims. That is a lot of money. And this does not include the necessary rehabilitation costs. At times it was overwhelming. If it was only the external obstacles to deal with, that would be hard enough. But then there were mornings where the internal, mental struggle would start early. Nagging negativity would invade, incessantly. It would be like an air raid of relentless attacks. The 'bombs' would explode with questions that sounded more like irrefutable statements calculated to undermine, mock, and discourage.

Who do you think you are? You think you can do this? What qualifies you to do this? You don't know what you're doing. You are bound to fail!

Note the not so subtle move from questions to the twisted conclusion that is by no means inevitable, but it sure sounds like it is. Give it some airtime and the shrapnel could terminate and maim the mission of hope before it had even got traction.

What is it that motivates in those moments? What can be of help? How can the heavy burden be lifted? Well, there is no one size fits all solution.

Nor do they all work in an instant. It takes investment of time, energy, and will. For those who want something, anything, to work, and are not mired in their unshakeable negative conclusions, there are positive things that can be done to return to a healthy focus. It could be a lightning, positive, thought that flies across the sky of the mind. Actually, to quote an ancient thought, 'When the Student is ready, the Teacher will come.'

Another unforgettable phrase was worth plenty of airtime for meditation. When Douglas was battling negative thoughts and emotions, regrets and fears, he took a solitary sentence from C.S. Lewis, to call a halt to the downward spiral to the inner abyss of the mind. The insidious attacks had a double-edged purpose – to birth despondency and despair which aborts any true self-worth and to kill any hope of being an instrument for good. Imprisoned and victimized by the downside effects of the negative, or positive, events of life. It takes a strong medicine to pierce the darkness, but these words were an effective antidote to the poison within,

'Humility is not Thinking Less of Yourself, but Thinking of Yourself Less.'

The external struggles against obstacles that come against plans for good are nothing compared this internal strife. In that classic film *Chariots of Fire*, Eric Liddell's voice is the narration for his triumphant Olympic 400 meter run. It was another message that points to an inner war,

'And where does this power come from to finish the race? It comes from within.'

Where does this courage come from, this fortitude? How is it stirred? For Douglas and John, it could come in a myriad of ways. It could be a line in a book. A lyric in a song. A memory of another occasion when one was between a rock and a hard place - and out of nowhere a solution was found. A phone call from a friend. A phone call to a friend. A brisk walk. A twenty-minute nap. A prayer. Listing the wonderful things in life they had seen and experienced. Dwelling on these things, and being grateful for them. Taking delight in them. Stooping to gaze at a flower, breathing in the fragrance, or enjoying the wonder of the color. Hearing a bird sing. Pausing longer than a cursory few seconds to fully embrace a sunset. Rising before sunrise to take in the dawn.

John Mullen and Douglas Bowman had another ace in the hole they used – to contemplate Florencia's ever-so-daily plight – that could jump start the day and get beyond the daunting immensity of the task. To spend a few moments imagining her, travel in the mind's eye to her village, was the best antidote to the mental melancholic 'selfie' that can settle in for a few hours or days.

Within a few days, the writers did not have to imagine any longer. Aderito uploaded video and photos from his visit. The excitement was almost tangible. But the thrill of that day paled when compared to a discovery just a few days later. It seemed, like any exploit, this was going to a roller coaster of highs and lows. The next high was off the charts. Thanks to Google, persistence and chance.

About four pages into a search on prosthetics was a heading, 'Jaipur Foot'. One click took Douglas and John into a whole new world of possibility for Florencia. It made for staggering reading. Jaipur Foot could produce a prosthetic leg for a below the knee amputee for $50 dollars. There was more. It looked like a normal leg, as opposed to robot-like prosthetics that Douglas and John had seen in pictures. Not only that, the amputee could bathe with the prosthetic, unlike the expensive ones that called for extra expense to get an additional prosthetic for bathing. There was more. It was FREE to the amputee, a true gift. Even more amazing, amputees came from all over India with their families, and food plus accommodation were provided at no charge to anyone. It does not happen too frequently that things that are too good to be true, actually, are true.

John composed an email to DR Mehta, Chief Patron of Jaipur Foot, simply sharing Florencia's story and the needs of the 10,000 Mozambican innocent victims, suffering for years. Their lives could change significantly, with a prosthetic. Was there something that they could do for Florencia? John clicked send and the email was off to Jaipur. It was a waiting game once again.

Within a day John had the reply. It resonated caring and concern for Florencia. It read like a letter from Mahatma Gandhi. It certainly was soaked in his values and gentleness. He offered Florencia a leg at no cost if it could be arranged for her to travel to Jaipur. As if that was not more than enough, DR Mehta wanted to help the rest of Mozambique amputees receive similar prosthetics. John and Douglas were stunned. He offered to train, free of charge, prosthetic technicians from Mozambique, who could then return to create a permanent clinic. As a further option, Jaipur Foot could send a team from India and put on a camp for one month to put limbs on five hundred amputees.

The two authors sat, silent, with a deep sense of awe. To them, this gesture of magnanimity was, indeed, a sign and a wonder. "We are on our way!" They exclaimed simultaneously.

What kind of man would do this?

Why? For an anonymous girl in the bush of Africa? At the request of two unknown men, thousands of miles away, on another continent?

Chapter 11

Crushed But Not Conquered

*One who gains strength by overcoming obstacles possesses
the only strength which can overcome adversity.*

~Albert Schweitzer

The role of chance and design is a source of debate. Accident and intention kiss and kill in the drama of life. The landmine is a device of destructive intention. The designers know full well its purpose. They may not know the particular destination on the earth but they do guarantee its effectiveness.

The ones who plant the device may have no idea of the identity of the one who will tread on the mine, but they are confident of the result. The unlucky person, the victim, is the one who, accidentally, puts their foot a few inches to the left or right of their normal path and, seconds later, is maimed for life. They may be minus a foot, one or two legs, or an arm, scarred inside and out, for the rest of their days. They had no idea that their customary walk to fetch water that day would be their last.

Complete accident? Well, no and yes. If they are unfortunate enough to be the poorest of the poor, their future just ended in the dirt of Mozambique. In other poor countries, the road to amputation is likely to be a car accident or diabetes. Regardless, the effect is the same.

Pandit Ram Chandra Sharma was enjoying himself teaching art and sculpting in Jaipur. Dr P.K. Sethi, an orthopedic surgeon at the SMS Hospital, called the master sculptor. 'Masterji' is Chandra's most popular name. It was an invitation to do some art therapy with some of his polio victims. 'Masterji' is one of those unique individuals who is always on the lookout for ways to improve the lives of those in need.

When Ram Chandra made his visits to the hospital he could not help noticing the costly and impractical 'limbs' for amputees. Masterji's mind started to get busy on a solution. He came up with a fresh creation. It was a foot constructed of vulcanized rubber hinged on a wooden limb. It was quick to make, light, and low cost. The foot gained the plaudits of the world and an award. The one thing it didn't gain was many users, about fifty in seven years. Masterji was largely forgotten and so was the foot.

Sadly, the screech of brakes and the inevitable crunching sound of metal on metal is like a contagious disease in the nation of India. It doesn't matter if it is a throbbing city like Jaipur, a small town, or a rural village, accidents are so, daily. They are the primary cause of amputations in the country of India. It is ironic to say this but one tragic accident has been the single most beneficial event to transform the life of amputees in India, and around the world.

Five hundred miles from the capital of India, New Delhi lies the small town of Jaisalmer. A mere 65,000 people live and work there. Yet this delightful urban setting in the heart of the desert region of Rajasthan is known as the 'Golden City.' The nickname is derived from the remarkable yellow sandstone architecture, that provides a sense of beauty and light. The magnificent Palace and impressive Temples that honor the Jain religion make Jaisalmer worth the trek for both pilgrim and tourist.

On a fateful, providential, day in 1969, a tragic accident left a tall, rangy, handsome man, crushed in a horrific car accident. It took extreme care to extricate his limp, almost lifeless, bloody body from the vehicle. He was rushed to the hospital where skilled doctors fought to save his leg and his life. Lying in the bed was DR Mehta, a young leader destined for big things in local and national financial departments. He had enjoyed a brilliant education, excelling on three continents. Yet, for all his accomplishments DR Mehta carried with him an awe-inspiring sense of humility and dignity. He was also determined and resilient, qualities he needed in abundance as the long road of recovery began to emerge from those dark days immediately after the accident. His leg was smashed and broken into forty pieces. Recovery would require arduous months in the hospital and then longer in grueling rehabilitation.

The crash had almost taken away the career of a man who would rise to be Chairman of the Securities of India and be the main architect of the rapid economic rise of this, the largest democracy in the world. The progress that would be made under Mehta's leadership and successive Indian governments would prove to be astounding. All of this was a long way off in a hospital bed of the invalid Mehta, or DR as many would call him. As he looked around DR could identify with Ram Chandra. The site of the nonstop procession of poor, lame, amputees vainly trying to get help had the same profound effect. It was as if Mehta 'woke up' to that other side of India, the helpless and the hopeless. A shaft of light from the heavens beamed into his soul and a message dawned on his mind, Mehta grasped a shocking reality.

If I had lost my leg I would have been able to pay for a prosthetic, but if my driver had lost his leg, what would he have done? He would have lost his leg, lost his job, his future and, probably ended up a beggar.

In the early days of recovery, Mehta devoured books. He loved reading and, besides, what else was there to do? One of his first reads was *Reach for the Sky*, the gripping story of Douglas Bader, a British pilot shot down in

World War II who lost both his legs, but with the aid of homemade, metal, legs got back into the war and became a decorated pilot. That would give courage to anybody, particularly this young Indian, fighting against pain and uncertainty. Like Bader, Mehta would not give up.

Mehta began to think deeply about suffering, and especially the poor, and those amputees without limbs. Two key practitioners of empathy and compassion, whose words he read over and over again, were Albert Schweitzer and Mahatma Gandhi. Schweitzer was a phenomenal, true witness to the impact of the message of Jesus on a man's life. Doctor, theologian, philosopher, musician and missionary – Schweitzer remains one of the most remarkable Christians of the twentieth century. He was awarded a Nobel Peace Prize and his speech, 'The Problems of Peace,' is thought by many to be one of the best Nobel speeches of all time. DR Mehta's life was undergoing a metamorphosis: specifically, his understanding of the priority of friendship and service with the suffering ones. This is not as an act of condescending compassion, but of compassionate solidarity. The contrast between the two is as wide as the Grand Canyon. More than that, the poor detect the difference, immediately.

Giving out of guilt does do some good, but can only provide a temporary satisfaction. It lacks substance. Charity from a sense of guilt is a feeble substitute for giving from a heart of love. The absolving of our guilt for personnel possessions speaks far louder than the 'gift' shared, no matter how large the gift. Humility and grace are found in those who know the pleasure of 'being with the poor' rather than the opportunity of 'giving to the poor.'

One quote of Schweitzer left an indelible mark on DR, 'Let us join the fraternity of those who bear the mark of pain.' Another from Mahatma Gandhi underscored the Schweitzer's outlook, 'Vaishnav jan to, tene kahiye,' which means 'A Good man is one who senses the pain of the other.' This period in recovery physically was reframing the core of Mehta's view of the essential meaning of a human life, and how it is to be lived, regardless of occupation or career, age or status.

*

DR Mehta finally returned to the work that would take him into the higher echelons of government service.

He also began to volunteer at Jaipur Foot Clinic.

Chapter 12

A Conspiracy of Kindness

The best way to find yourself is to lose yourself
in the service of others.

~ Mahatma Gandhi

Aderito Ismael was clearly shocked and delighted at the 'news' about Jaipur Foot and the amazing offer of Dr. Mehta. John and Douglas wondered and reflected with Aderito, on a Skype call, what an astonishing chain of events. Florencia would now be presented with a fresh plan. India was on the horizon. She had never left her village. Now, she would be leaving her country, fly for the first time, and go to a place called Jaipur. All this because Katya Cengel went on a trek to Macachula, two men read an article online, and a Mozambique man put himself out, big time. In the many phone calls and emails it seemed like these three men had known each other for years instead of a matter of weeks.

At this point, John and Douglas put their rather 'selfie' book on hold. The book went into cold storage. They had found Florencia, and she had found them.

———

The names Leon and Eline are notorious in the history books of Mozambique. These two cyclones, one named after a man and one a woman, met on a blind date in the middle of the Indian Ocean. They went west together and reached the beaches and inland of Mozambique in February 2000. They became a tempestuous, fighting, married couple that united in explosive acrimony and wreaked total havoc on Mozambique. Even before Leon and Eline landed on the scene, Mozambique had lost 150 dead to flooding on a significant scale. This was like the perfect cyclone equivalent to the perfect storm. A marriage made in hell, that was Leon and Eline.

The narrow and shallow Limpopo river, normally a few hundred yards wide and a few feet deep was, suddenly, 12 miles wide and 10 feet deep. A dam broke in Chokwe in the middle of the night. This was the area's worst nightmare. After it was all over 700 people had died, the damage was estimated at $500 million, and well in excess of 330,000 citizens had been displaced. The effect of Leon and Eline was devastating to a country already finding the road to recovery tough and the demining, slow. This brought much of the work to a sudden, sodden, halt.

In the middle of this ordeal the story of one woman and her fortitude and endurance pulled the nation up by its bootstraps. It was poignant and spectacular. A young mother Carolina looked up as she was preparing dinner outside her hut. What she saw was frightening. She was nine months pregnant. In the distance, she saw a wall of mud and debris 'collecting' homes at breakneck speed and rapidly approaching her hut. The Limpopo had Carolina's home fixed in its sights. She shouted. She mobilized. She carried her child. Her amputee father and grandmother limped and ran for the safety of the tallest tree they could find. The swollen river rushed below them.

The floods had risen and her only refuge was to slowly clamber up into the top of the tree and clutch its branches to survive. She waited and waited. Darkness gave way to dawn. Then it did the same again, hour after tortuous hour. On the third morning, she was still holding on for two dear lives. It was hot. It was humid. Dehydration was dangerous to the neighbors on other branches. To Carolina, it could prove fatal. No one came. For those arduous days, she sat precariously on a branch as the rapids swirled dangerously below. Her greatest fear was drowning in the waters below. It was a fear well-founded. Tragically, Carolina's grandmother had lost her grip and fell to her death in the dirty flood.

For three days she had no water or food. Carolina was twenty feet in the air on her green 'bed' and with Mother Nature's clock ticking, and a baby kicking. Various members of the family were positioned in the two Marfura trees. On that third morning, up the tree with no food or water, she gave birth. Special teams were searching all of Carolina's region for any survivors. In a stroke of luck, a helicopter pilot of the South African Air Force looked out of his window and saw the temporary tree house and birthing center. Carolina had just given birth. He returned to base and picked up an army medic. Forty minutes later the helicopter lifted mother and baby from the tree. The picture of a young soldier and the baby being hoisted into the helicopter went around the world, to every news agency. This was prior to YouTube and Facebook, and before the word viral was invented for successful networking. This photo did indeed go 'viral.' It was front and center of newspapers and the focus of television news stations.

After a couple of months, the recovery of Mozambique was not going well. Countries had been giving to Kosovo and Rwanda, for their respective needs. Some money and resources came in but nothing compared to the amount that would be required. A newspaper in London and one in Washington sponsored Carolina and her baby to travel to England and America. In a few days in London 30 million pounds was raised and in Washington 40 million dollars. Many politicians in Mozambique regarded those two weeks as the tipping point in the recovery. It took a country in abject misery and despair to one with renewed confidence and hope.

As John and Douglas recalled Carolina's tale, it pointed then towards a dramatic shift in thinking. Uppermost in their minds was how they could raise funds to meet the needs meet the needs of all Mozambique landmine victims, hidden in villages.

They were not up a tree, like Carolina, but they were still stuck - waiting for help. Why not write Florencia's story instead of their book? Her story would be worth telling and could help them provide the 10,000 other innocent victims with a leg. Yes, it was obvious, but, first things first - they needed to get her a leg.

Aderito called a few days later. He had news. It was not good news. Great ideas are often confronted with negative and discouraging events or information. Florencia was not even registered as a citizen! Like many rural villages, Macachula's records were more oral than written. She needed to be registered. Aderito was already anticipating the challenges of bureaucracy and communication. His tone told the writers everything. This was not going to be plain sailing. Not by any means. Once registered, the next step, and not one necessarily any easier, was for Florencia to obtain a passport. Well, that really meant Aderito would have his work cut out, trying to pay attention to his own difficult situation and, at the same time, drive hundreds of miles, fill in forms, and navigate the various agencies.

There was one consoling thought to Douglas and John in all of this. Without discovering Aderito they wouldn't have had a prayer of even getting this far. Gratitude and concentrating on the positive builds a wall against adversity and adversaries. Besides, Aderito had told Douglas and John, "Don't worry guys, it will take time, but we will get there. And, I want you both to know, whatever my situation, I make this commitment to you, I will take Florencia to India and get her a leg. That is my personal promise." If words like those don't lift the spirits and prepare one to be patient and persevere, nothing will.

DR Mehta found himself thinking more and more about Jaipur Foot. The taste of volunteering had grown way beyond spending one day per week at the facility. It had become his passion and his calling. When the right man, with the appropriate talents, experience, and vision, finds the one task for which he has been uniquely prepared, something very special is always likely to occur. At Jaipur Foot it did, and then some! From fitting fifty prosthetics in seven years, DR took Jaipur Foot from limbo to a whole new dimension of growth in the number and quality of prosthetics, to become the number one prosthetic fitting organization in the world.

Mehta used his vast experience to grow the whole organization but did it from the radical foundation of philanthropic values. He decided to put the poorest people first in his consideration, before organization, staff, and buildings. DR right from the outset made an astounding move to provide free food and lodging not only for the amputee but for any accompanying family that had come from all over India. In time, over thirty percent of the workers were those who have suffered limb loss. The speed with which they move about their business is the best advertisement for the prosthesis they now help produce. Jaipur has the feel of a large healing community where all men and women are not only believed to be equal, but can be seen and sensed every day. In fact, the ones regarded as the least are treated as special in Jaipur, the food and water are free to the poor, while Mehta even pays for his own water bottle from his pension. He takes nothing away from Jaipur Foot, except the sight of the lame and miserable walking out beaming with joy. John and Douglas could hardly contain themselves as they read more and more about DR Mehta and the work of Jaipur.

Jaipur Foot makes everyone feel important, even if they are, manifestly, poor. Indeed, to him, they are the most important ones. Healing and Joy are the treasures found here by the disabled and the amputee. This is where those who come are blown away by the winds of love and kindness. The former victim identity and the sense of being no use to anyone are swept away by the flow of affirmation. Douglas found some words that sum up the rich legacy of DR Mehta, words penned by a woman who also rose out of the dark shadows of life to be a beacon for her nation and beyond. The distinguished American poet, Maya Angelou, writes,

'I've learned that people will forget what you said, people will forget what you did, but people will never forget how you made them feel.'

DR Mehta makes the poor feel rich, very rich indeed.

Chapter 13

Seize The Day

Boys, you must strive to find your own voice. Because the longer you wait to begin, the less likely you are to find it at all. Thoreau said, "Most men lead lives of quiet desperation." Don't be resigned to that. Break out!

~John Keating, Dead Poets Society

D ane Holroyd had just returned from an assignment that involved hands-on support of a video project for a program that the National Football League had set up to help young people. As summer was fading he used every waking moment to surf, skateboard hang out with friends. Lying in bed at night he did occasionally give some thought to the upcoming school year. He had to, this would be his final year at the MAD Academy (Multimedia Arts and design academy at Santa Barbara High School).

Dane would need to come up with a Senior Project. His only thought was, *I must do something unusual and, maybe, about somebody doing good.* The familiar tones from Dane's mobile dragged his mind into the present.

He looked down and saw Dan Williams name on the small screen. Dan was director of his Academy. *Dan?* What could he want?

"Hi Dane, how was the NFL?

"Good. Learned a lot."

"Have you got a minute?"

"Yeah, no problem." Dane was all ears.

Dan went on to recount the bare details of his meeting with John and Douglas, Florencia's story was the appetizer. Then he got to the entree.

"It could mean going to India and Mozambique. How would you feel about that?"

"The story's solid.

To go and film it would be amazing. What a project. Count me in."

"Great. I couldn't see you turning down a chance like this. I have a couple of other people in mind, but who do you............"

Dane stopped Dan right there. "Samsun and Ella, definitely."

"You beat me to it, yes those were the two that immediately came to mind."

"Shall I text them?" Dane's brain was buzzing with excitement and could barely restrain himself at the opportunity that had been set before him.

"Yes, go ahead - I can't imagine them not being up for something like this. Let me know how you get on. Oh, one other thing. The two guys leading the team would love to get together with both of us to explore this further. I'll let you know when it is arranged. Sounds cool, don't you think?"

"Oh man, I can't wait for school to start! See ya."

Dane was beside himself. India and Mozambique, this was going to be awesome. Selling the idea to Samsun took about the same amount of time as Dan pitching the possibility to Dane.

The beginnings of a team were emerging, Landon, John's son had attended MAD. John mentioned to Douglas the idea that savvy social media guys might be interested in doing something worthwhile. They had met with Dan and the possibility of HOW and MAD working together for the good of Florencia and landmine victims. HOW International, which stands for Help One Walk, had been set up as a nonprofit by John and Douglas with a view to giving prosthetic legs to landmine victims and developing lifetime humanitarians. The meeting with Dan was excellent. He mentioned Dane as a distant possibility to go on the mission and film. Douglas and John were energized by this new development. However, it was soon tempered when they heard from Aderito. He had no good news to report from his latest round of travels. He had become well used to waiting to see an official, only to hear, 'oh, you need so 'n' so, not me, I can't help you.' So 'n' so could be 500 kilometers away.

Dan Williams is not only Director at the MAD Academy, in the sense of coordinating programs, students and staff. He is much more than that. He's an educational entrepreneur. When he sees anything that could produce an educational opportunity, his entrepreneurial instincts perk up and perfectly match his leadership skills. He is ever mindful that graduates from the program should not merely have successful careers, but catch a vision for giving back locally and internationally.

This possible partnership with HOW International would potentially provide a healthy outlet for students; learning about a global problem, writing articles, designing media, blogging, speaking, and creating short videos. In many ways, the collaboration and teamwork required were the very nature of what a media academy should be all about. After all, most of those graduating, would, eventually, be working in an environment where skills alone would not make it. It was also important to know how to be a team player. This project to change the world of an innocent victim on another continent could prove just such an opportunity, and something for which MAD Academy students and the high school itself could be justifiably proud.

Dane and Samsun were like many duos who work together, each bringing a completely different perspective and talent to the partnership and their projects. Dane seemed to have an instinct for creativity that simply cannot be learned. Application and mentoring by experienced media pros might help develop him but he has that X factor that money cannot buy and overdoing the education could harm. Samsun brought a determined 'know-how' to projects, certainly not without ideas of his own, but he has great potential in making the concepts work in interpreting transitions of sight and sound.

Douglas and John brought on two Brooks Institute graduates to help lead the video team. Brook's was a premier film and photography school that consistently graduated some of the finest filmmakers in the world. Ben Johnson and Brett Bollier were no exceptions. Their newly formed business, Culture Spark, would provide the high-level engineering, editing, and production needed to create promotional videos for HOW and the team.

It didn't take much persuasion for Ella Deardorff to decide she wanted to have some role in helping Florencia get a leg and a new life. One short text from Dane inviting Ella was all she needed to say yes to using her photographic skills on two continents and for a worthy humanitarian cause. No doubt this mission would entail some hardships and challenges of remote situations, where the people would not be living the American Riviera life of Santa Barbara. The thought of a daughter traveling thousands of miles to two developing countries can produce any amount of stress and anxiety in a parent. Ella's mom was quite the opposite. She was excited and proud at the prospect of Ella moving out and for such a good cause. Dads can take a bit more of a conservative approach to such a venture. Ella's dad was a little hesitant at first, but once he saw Ella's passion he not only accepted it, he too was thrilled at his daughter's compassion for Florencia and the courage to launch into the mission. One week later Dan Williams met up with Tanner Mees in San Francisco. Tanner was another student entering his final year at MAD. Once again Florencia's story and the prospect of traveling to India and Mozambique was greeted with a resounding yes.

Through a fascinating turn of events and emails John got in touch with Debra Larsen, the Dean of Engineering at California Polytechnic University at San Luis Obispo, John Mullen's alma mater. He was also made aware of the remarkable QL+ Lab. This tremendous facility and program is the brainchild of Jon Monett, an alumnus from the School of Engineering. The lab's goal was to encourage a pool of students from the various disciplines of engineering to create real time solutions for veterans who were struggling with a prosthetic or allied issue. This was a 'learn by doing' on innovation that required interviews with the veteran, assessment of the needs and requirements and, finally, a potential product or alteration that would make life so much easier for the client. John had an opportunity to share the story of the beginnings of HOW, which of course, ironically, was directly related to Katya Cengel from the Journalism Program. Dr. Lily Lihao, of the engineering department, coordinated the special Interdisciplinary Senior Project Program. She invited John and Douglas to submit a proposal. They had only a few days to submit a project description.

To say this was out of the blue would be an understatement. By this point, John and Douglas were getting used to looking for accidents. This one was far too good an opportunity to pass up. The HOW International challenge: to create a fully functional below the knee prosthetic leg that looked like a normal leg and that could be manufactured for fifty dollars. It would be a tall order, but the engineering students at Cal Poly had a reputation for doing outstanding and innovative work.

John and Douglas made one decision very quickly. It was an easy no-brainer.

Since neither of them had any in-depth knowledge of the human biomechanics or engineering details regarding any prosthetic devices they would concentrate on what they did know. Well, the main thing they knew was not a what, but a who, Florencia Artur. They could tell her story, with some images. Douglas had been collecting video of the Jaipur Foot in action - a small boy climbing a tree and two older men, both with prosthetics, sprinting inside DR Mehta's facility. It was electrifying. Douglas and John had researched the costs of prosthetics in Mozambique and the U.S. They also had a photo that had been created to show some young women models all with one or two prosthetics. The total cost for the twelve 'models' that the U.S. Government would have to pay in their lifetime would be in the region of 16 million dollars. And that is ONLY for their health care and rehabilitation. If Florencia had been a returning veteran from Iraq or Afghanistan, it would cost the U.S. government around $1.4 million dollars on her leg, health and therapy alone for a lifetime. In one sense this is good. But what if the returning veteran had a choice? Instead of all that money being spent on her leg she could choose to go for a more basic functional leg, even spend a month in India, see the Taj Mahal, be given a new leg, but put the rest of the government's money into a well-designed house, invest in a business, educate her children and provide for her grandchildren.

Douglas and John were shocked at the kind of money that needed to be spent on a prosthetic to rival the $50 dollar Jaipur Foot, which looked like a leg and with which you could walk into a shower. Not many women like to look like a robot and with the Jaipur Foot they could wear tights or pants and be fashionable. In fact, in the USA, a second prosthetic would be necessary for showering at a further cost of 1,000 dollars. Only the rich amputees shower on two legs in America. And why should amputees injured for any reason have to argue and fight with government agencies or insurers? Should the Obamacare guidelines regarding pre-existing conditions or provisions for amputees change with a fresh administration, good luck to the amputees of the future. The poor and hidden will suffer and return to their wheelchair. They are unlikely to have a new leg, and, for many, any future leg.

To describe India in words like, 'Third World' or 'Developing Country,' accompanied by a singular derogatory tone, makes more of a comment about the speaker or writer than the country. In many areas, India is at the forefront of engineering, medical development, media, meditation, philanthropy, and literature. No doubt, in this, the largest democracy on the face of the earth, monumental poverty and problems remain. But that is one side of the story. So, why are they so creative in India? A $2000 (yes, that's two thousand dollars) car? Done. And the other manufacturers who scoffed are now choking on their words and chasing after the Indian engineers, suitably humbled.

These engineers and innovators have a mantra that underscores a philosophy of life.

It is not about value for money. It's about value for the many.

DR Mehta's definition and foundation of 'health care' is to be heart centered and empowered by love. From that deep core stems an outlook that embraces the whole person.

It can best be said in his words: "Anyone who loses their leg and dignity innocently should not have to pay to get it back." And in Jaipur they don't have to pay. More than that they are given food and lodging at no cost.

Somehow in America, 'value for many' winds up being renamed socialism and ridiculed by many of those who can afford their insurance. It always helps to name something an 'ism,' such as Communism, Capitalism, or Socialism. This blocks decent dialogue about how to help people in its tracks. Then it suddenly becomes complicated to provide a leg.

The only conclusion to draw from the oft quoted phrase, 'where there is a will there's a way,' is that currently, in terms of healthcare, there is no 'will' to provide for all amputees. Maybe it's because it demands a sacrifice on the part of every citizen to share together to give my neighbor a leg. Some would say, 'Yes that's the way, the government should not be involved. The church and local communities should do this out of the goodness of their heart.' Well, sad though it is, neither of those groups had the compassion or will to provide a leg and the ability to walk for thousands of fellow American amputees. And insurance wasn't working for vast numbers of the unfortunate amputees. Regardless of all the other 'ins and outs,' and cries of, 'oh my premium has gone up,' 'oh I can't have the doctor I want,' these previously ignored or turned away before 2010, have the Affordable Care Act and its architect, President Obama, to thank as they walk around their neighborhood. No wheelchair. No crutch.

Imagine it, able to walk hand in hand with their wife or daughter, husband or son.

Imagine doing nothing.

Chapter 14

Drawing the Future

You can look at a picture for a week and never think of it again.
You can also look at a picture for a second and think of it all your life.

~Joan Miro

Delay is the soil that can produce doubt. Inevitably, there began to be some hints at, and occasional discussions on, the advisability of delaying the trip. Perhaps, until the school spring break vacation. That was more than six months away. It all made good sense, even wise. The tasks needing to be completed were mounting without any positive sign from Mozambique. It was a TO DO LIST nightmare. To find the necessary funds, arrange travel, obtain visas and accommodations. This was the height of craziness. Added to this, Florencia had no birth registration and would still need a passport.

Perspective changes everything.

Douglas and John couldn't help thinking of Florencia coping every day with a crippling disability. They had seen Aderito's pictures of Florencia.

Hoeing the ground; leaning on a broken crutch; washing saucepans; leaning on that same broken crutch; even carrying water on her head and somehow making it back to her hut. How could they even entertain the idea of going later? After all, this was not a Club Med vacation for students, or a sightseeing cultural tour. The purpose was clear, the team had a job to do. This was a mission of Justice (righting a wrong), and Compassion (a demonstration of practical love).

The two writers reminded themselves of their core beliefs. What if it was their sister or daughter? Wasn't doing 'The Golden Rule' the first line of the HOW Constitution? If HOW International declared themselves 'end-user obsessed,' this was a test of that priority, and an examination of Douglas and John's resolve. They must hold their nerve, and, say quite a few prayers.

They scanned the schedule for the Cal Poly project presentations. They had drawn the short straw. They were allotted the very last presentation on the last day. By the time they arrived at the front of the classroom for their project presentation; a few students had left, some were sleeping, others looking bored and everyone was so ready for it to be over.

The opening video was compelling. It was a joint effort filmed and produced by the MAD and Culture Spark teams. More than a few of the audience woke up. Most at least sat up from their slumping position. John's telling of Florencia's tragic and poignant story could only be described as powerful. Douglas, with a neat touch of British passion and humor, demonstrated just what the Jaipur Foot could do for an amputee who loved soccer - and just how much an American amputee would need to pay to do the same thing. John began to speak of Jaipur Foot and then he put on the clip of the boy climbing a tree and the men sprinting. You could hear gasps and a few whisper loudly, "Oh, my God!"

John mentioned if HOW were selected they would take one of the team to Jaipur. Then Douglas put up on the large screen THE PHOTO. He let it stay there, for thirty seconds. He didn't say a word. The room fell silent.

On the screen was the image of a small African boy sitting on a concrete floor. He's using thick white chalk to outline two legs on the cement. The legs are perfect. His are not. The chalk lines extend from his two stumps. After what seemed like eternity, Douglas finally spoke. "This boy is not imagining a pole out of his legs. He's imagining a real leg. If a small

boy could imagine this, what could senior engineers imagine?"

The room went silent. There was a gasp. No one knew how to respond. It was as if the boy was sitting in the room making his request known. Some students wiped away a tear trying not to be noticed. Like many of these engineers, John and Douglas were emotionally drained.

Now, all they could do was wait.

A couple of days after the presentation John picked Douglas up in his SUV and informed him that Aderito had text to say that he would Skype them at 7:00 am. It was now 6:45 am. They sped up the hill to a beachside area of Santa Barbara known as the Mesa. Many homes in this neighborhood have splendid views of the signature Santa Barbara Harbor and waterfront bay.

The SUV occupants had no time to gaze at the local spectacle. John and Douglas had a deadline, and it was minutes away. They needed Wi- Fi connection to receive the call from Aderitio. They breathed a sigh of relief when parking space became available directly in front of Starbucks. The relief turned to grins when the Wi-Fi signal proved strong even in the SUV. They didn't feel bad about using the signal. The SUV had driven away many times with a latte or flat white in its cup holders, and after Aderito's call it would drive away with the usual two Grande drinks.

The sight that greeted John and Douglas was a smiling Aderito and something they had not expected. Florencia was sitting quietly behind Aderito. The two writers' friend held a document in his hand and one didn't have to know any Portuguese to understand this was the document everyone had been waiting to see. Aderito repeated to John and Douglas that he had given Florencia another detailed description of the events that had now spanned five months. John asked Aderito to pass on to Florencia his sincere sadness at her experience but profound hope that soon she would walk once again. Douglas was so glad that he had the foresight to video the video of the call. It was astonishing. John went on to express his gratitude for the patience and fortitude of Aderito to arrive at this landmark moment. Ever the practical realist as well as cheerful optimist, Aderito soon brought a note of sobriety to the early morning headiness. He had been told it could take up to forty-five days, maybe more to obtain a passport for Florencia. There was silence in the SUV. He would start the process, immediately. If it could be done at all, HOW had the right man in Aderito Ismael.

Douglas and John had a coffee and then set about preparing for their 10:30 am meeting with the ever expanding MAD team, many of whom served tirelessly behind the scenes, even though they would not be going on the mission. Dan, who had been busy that morning came to chat with John and Douglas at the end of the thirty minutes. He explained that another senior student would like to go on the trip. Luke O'Neil's mother was seriously ill, but it had long been her dream, since her son Luke was a small boy, that one day he would travel to Africa. Luke's mother and father asked Dan if it might be at all possible to add Luke to the team. John and Douglas had no hesitation. Five MAD students and Dan would now be bound for India and Mozambique. Also joining the team, late on, was Landon, John's son. Landon was a very recent MAD graduate and John's primary connection with Dan. In fact, Landon had played soccer with a couple of the guys going. He would be a good addition.

An email from Dr. Lihao confirmed that HOW's low-cost prosthetic project had been selected. The note listed five senior students, Brian Murphy, Derek Morgan, Domonique Porcincula, Kendall Ruggles, and Chris Aguayo.

A few weeks later after a couple of Skype calls John and Douglas made their way to John's old stomping ground, California Polytechnic at San Luis Obispo. The students spent some time outlining the areas of research that might constitute the greatest chance of success and were busy splitting up the specific tasks. An additional surprise to John and Douglas was that the University would fund three of the students to go to Jaipur leaving HOW to sponsor Brian, coordinator of the team and Dom who would come from Madrid where he was spending a semester abroad. Ben and Brett of Culture Spark did some excellent filming and photography of the meeting and everyone went out for an early dinner that evening.

During the project launch dinner, Ben Johnson interviewed the students focusing on what motivated them to choose this particular project. Kendall, the only woman on the team was interviewed after the decision and she shared, 'I saw that picture of the boy and ahh…I knew I just had to do this project.' Brian was looking for something different, and this was it. 'I wanted to do something that would do meet more than the bottom line. And to be involved in a project that would have an impact in the world.'

Although somewhat tentative, the only real window of opportunity to travel to Jaipur, India, and Mozambique was the Thanksgiving school vacation. The initial plan was to travel to Mozambique with the media students and join up with Aderito, then head up to collect Florencia and film her departure from Macachula and Maputo Airport en route to Jaipur. The whole exercise was fraught with problems, most of them very large. There was the change in time zones and the hours in the air flying over twenty-five thousand miles. Then, there was the 'hope' that there would be no issues with Florencia's prosthetic, particularly because the right leg had been amputated above the knee. Below the knee amputations do not have quite the same complications. It was a concern: flights needed to be booked. That raised one of the other major obstacles that perennially plague a non-profit. Money. How in the world could they financially make it happen?

The two writers, now accidental humanitarians, were caught in a situation where failure, on this mission, would not just be embarrassing, it would be an unmitigated disaster. For Florencia herself, Aderito and Victoria, Florencia's family and their village, Dan Williams and the Mad students and parents, the Mad Academy, the Cal Poly Seniors and Faculty,

Douglas and John and their friends, and DR Mehta and Jaipur Foot. The list was endless. The prospect was too frightening to entertain. Yet the odds did not seem in favor of these two humanitarians. This was out of their comfort zones. Even for a seasoned entrepreneur like John, and for Douglas, for whom launching out into the unknown was certainly not unfamiliar. Fortunately, there were not too many days where fear or panic took them by surprise. The course of the lives of these two men had prepared them for the inevitable ups and downs. Truth be told, most of the time they were busy working with MAD and arranging meetings with people who had real interest in the objectives of HOW.

The small booklet with embossed gold printing and the gleaming white teeth of the smile on Aderito Ismael's face gave the news away, before the most beautiful words that John and Douglas longed to hear were spoken. "Guys, we have it, Florencia's Passport." Considering the many failed and dropped Skype calls, and those others where the reception was clear but the content negative, everything about this call was perfect.

John and Douglas didn't know whether to laugh or cry, or do both. The sudden relief, from the weight of stress and a lack of sleep, will do that to you. This day was doubly special for Douglas. It was his sixty-fourth birthday. What a gift. This was extraordinary. It had cost Aderito more than he cared to say; time, energy, frustration, and stress. But he had done it. He had come up trumps yet again.

Chapter 15

Hitting the Wall

A garden is a grand teacher. It teaches patience and careful watchfulness: it teaches industry and thrift: above all it teaches entire trust.

~Gertrude Jekyll

Douglas told Aderito he thought he was Tom Cruise, Superman and Jesus rolled into one. It was only a slight exaggeration.

Aderito showed Florencia's passport photo and information, even the blank pages were exciting. It was a short-lived moment of joy for the three friends. The mission was on but there was so much to do and barely four weeks to do it all. Everything had to fall into place perfectly to be ready for a Thanksgiving that would rival any these travelers had experienced in their lives. Certainly, it was one of the most unusual. As John drove Douglas home they both sensed that a hope could yet become a reality. A 'YouCaring.com' fundraising site had been set up and John was busy sending out news that what had been a tentative plan now needed funds and Florencia could be walking again before Christmas. Emails were sent, video appeals created, and it was an all-hands-on-deck call to action.

The days following produced a fresh set of concerns. One of those descended like fog on a gloomy day in November. Everyone would need visas for India but the team that would return with Florencia to Mozambique would need a visa for both countries. The Indian visa could be obtained online so it appeared to present no problem. The Mozambique visa would be stamped in each passport sent to the Mozambique Embassy in Washington DC. However, when Douglas was looking at the visa forms, one detail was critical, a date for arrival and departure for India and Mozambique, as well as the ports for each respectively. Combine a BHAG (Big Hairy Audacious Goal) with a BLOC (Big Lack of Cash), and throw in time constraints, dependence on governments, delivery services, and this is a recipe for a nerve-racking experience.

Fielding normal questions from students and parents when no satisfactory answer is available can be particularly unsettling. 'I'm not sure,' or, worse still 'I don't know,' never sits well. All that is left is to plan for it working out and do one's utmost. John and Douglas worked and waited. They worked and they waited. Slowly funds started to come in. Nine dollars was given by a friend of Landon's, a student at Chapman University. Sometimes it could be a gift of 5,000 dollars. Every dollar counted, and every person valued.

Douglas was sitting at his desk about to tear some of his plentiful hair out. He had checked fares and flights and hit a wall. He would have loved to have taken credit for the revelation that flashed across his mind. It came out of nowhere, and it was a game changer. Occasionally, when we are at the end of our rope, at the moment of utter desperation and our brain is shot, it happens. A smile as big as Aderito's lit up the small office. 'Of course, the team don't have to go to Mozambique then Jaipur, we could fly from LAX to Delhi, on to Jaipur and then go from Jaipur to Mozambique. If the guys from MAD want to film Florencia leaving her village or walking in the village they could reenact the departure at the time of her homecoming. It would make the times of travel doable and save thousands of dollars.' Entrepreneurs must not only be seeking funds; they must save funds. This latter task is of equal importance to the former, if a nonprofit is to prosper.

In any start-up company cash flow is a significant issue. A start up non-profit with no product to trade needs time to develop. Help One Walk was a fledgling little bird, two months old, planning to embark on a flight half way around the world, on a wing and a prayer. In many ways, it was sheer madness. The costs alone would be between $35,000 and $53,000 dollars to get to Mozambique, then Jaipur, back to Mozambique and, finally, return to California. Now, at least the trip was simplified. Six months earlier John and Douglas were minding their own book and didn't have a business. Now they had a BHAG on their plate – pull off a trip that was a few weeks away, no travel arrangements made and a severe shortage of the money required. It had been a couple of decades since Douglas read some simple, but powerful words. They would alter his whole outlook on life; 'What would you do if you were ten times more bold?' Essentially, life became a laboratory instead of a classroom. Sometimes following through on an instinct produced amazing results. Not being an exact science there were those other times which could be somewhat embarrassing. One might say they were 'learning moments.' Yet, Douglas and Fiona had seen so many miracles that made the learning moments worth it. Douglas pondered the line between boldness and stupidity. To Douglas, it was thin, very, very thin. And some days he couldn't tell on which side of the line he was standing.

An instinctive idea can provide a solution that may never have dawned on the linear thinker. In a similar way, connecting with an individual of an organization may hold the key to whether a project will meet with success, or not. The wise entrepreneur knows what he, or she, doesn't know. When the instinctive idea combines with another's expertise the chances of success are greatly increased. Douglas unconsciously reached into his memory bank. On the whiteboard of his mind, three bold letters were written by black Sharpie, STA. Douglas didn't need any help with the interpretation – The Student Travel Association.

Discovering Jennifer Raleigh Bills, at Student Travel was like finding a pure pearl in an ocean of fake pearls. For Jennifer, customer service isn't a job title or position – it's a passion that expresses itself in a professional and determined dedication to satisfy her customers. Jennifer was able to guide Douglas through a tapestry of options and narrow down the ones that would work for HOW and the travelers leaving at all manner of different times, days and routes. More than that, the students could purchase insurance coverage at a ridiculously low rate, and it would be valid for one year. The decisive value that STA brought to Douglas was the ability to book flights with a deposit. Cash was coming in, but not quickly enough to pay for all the necessary flights. Jennifer worked tirelessly to work out any kinks and obtain the optimum travel options. Whether it was merely faith or fate, things were beginning to look good for departures and arrivals for everyone's schedule.

With the tickets finalized except for the little matter of payment, it was time to check everyone had applied for an Indian visa. Douglas heard from Brian at Cal Poly that Chris was having trouble obtaining a visa for India. John and Douglas perused the passports of the team going to Mozambique. Photos were checked. The forms were proofread. Douglas bought an overnight envelope at Federal Express, inside was enclosed an overnight envelope for the return, and the check. He sent them off to the Mozambique Embassy in Washington DC.

It was Thursday. Eight days to go.

Things were going smoothly and all was in order. Finally, Douglas and John could feel a calm anticipation as the trip grew closer. One gap in the organization that Douglas had not managed to close was the train tickets from Delhi to Jaipur. Both Douglas and John spent a couple of hours on hold with the ticket agency in India, to no avail. They would have to be purchased on arrival.

All continued to go well until Tuesday morning. It was early so Douglas thought that he would check to see if the passports had been stamped at the Mozambique Embassy. No answer. He tried again one hour later. No response. *Oh well no problem*, thought Douglas. *It's probably in the mail.*

On Wednesday, Douglas and John left the customary MAD Meeting at 11:00 am. The thirty minute get together had gone well. Douglas and John had a final meeting with the parents of the MAD team. They both remarked on the enthusiasm of the parents for the mission, By that Wednesday more than $36,000 had been donated. When they returned, Douglas called the Embassy. He was hoping not to annoy them. Nevertheless, he did want to confirm the passports had been sent in the overnight Fed Ex pre-paid package. There was no reply from the visa department. Douglas began to get slightly anxious. He found the Embassy website and called another department. No answer and the voicemail was full. Seven more departments produced no live voices and all with a voice indicating the voicemail box was full. Now Douglas was no longer merely concerned, he was becoming stressed to the max.

It was now 4:50 pm in Washington. If the passports were not sent that night, Thursday would be too late. The Fed Ex delivery didn't come until 10:30 am, the team needed to leave for Lax from Santa Barbara at 9:00 am the next morning. At 4:55 pm someone answered the phone. His relief lasted less than a minute. What he heard was alarming. The lady who answered the call informed Douglas that she could see the passports, unsigned on the desk in the consular office. Douglas nervously explained the urgency of the situation. If they were not sent tonight the trip could not take place. Tomorrow was useless. This was a mission to give a leg to a young single mother of Mozambique.

Despite the strength of Douglas words, the woman was sorry but there was no way anything could happen before noon the next day. Douglas put the phone down. For the next few hours, his mind was a rubber dinghy in a stormy sea. It was internal torture. They had come so far, overcome so much, and were on the verge of pulling off a remarkable feat. And now it lay in shreds.

Alone in his room, he vented his anger at the embassy staff. He was like a boxer who had been punched in the solar plexus and it had been followed by an uppercut. He was winded and wobbly on his knees. He went to bed. Sleep was not going to come anytime soon on this dark night. His mind would seize on every potential solution. *Maybe I could fly to Washington and get a red eye back and still be in time for the flight on Friday.* He checked the possibilities. It was impossible.

As he lay in bed he poured out his soul to God. He was George Bailey in *It's a Wonderful Life*, desperate and at the end of his rope.

George Bailey needed an angel, and so did Douglas.

Chapter 16

Darkness Before Dawn

It's always darkest right before the dawn.

~Anonymous

It was only twenty-four hours to departure. In the predawn hours of Friday morning, Douglas Bowman called the Mozambique Embassy in Washington, D.C. The receptionist who answered said she knew nothing about the passports or visas. Douglas probed and probed. The lady politely reiterated that she knew nothing. Douglas was about to put the phone down, and entertain his worst fears, when the woman said, "Wait, wait!"

"Hold on. Someone has just walked in and she works in that department. If you hold I will get her to speak to you."

Douglas held. What else could he do? The duration of the call on his iPhone read 03:00 minutes.

The bedroom was pitch black, except for the piercing light of the mobile. He sat in his cell. A prisoner on death row awaiting his last rites and meal. He dared not contemplate his Epitaph to be etched on his gravestone: 'He tried but failed.'

The iPhone read 05:27 for the call. It was like ten long agonizing minutes. From a deposit in his memory bank words flew down, like a carrier pigeon, and landed…Douglas, it's always darkest right before the dawn.

"Hello, Visa department."

Douglas was about to launch into yet another telling of the dire situation when the lady interrupted him.

"I'm Annabel. You spoke to me last night. I informed you that the office was closing in five minutes, and the next time for the visas to be processed would be at noon today."

Douglas reacted quickly. "But, you must do some…." The word 'something' was silenced.

"Could you just let me speak, Mr. Bowman?"

"I was the last one in the office. Everyone had left for the day. I had the keys in my hand. I got to thinking about how desperate you had sounded on the phone. I imagined the poor young woman in my country missing a leg. So, I didn't lock the door. I stepped back inside. I stamped all the passports with the visas, documented the personal details on our embassy dossier, and put it all in the overnight package. It was a fifteen-minute walk to the drop and I had no time to spare. I just made it in time. Mr. Bowman, the passports will be with you in Santa Barbara by 10:30 am this morning." Never had a dulcet African voice sounded more beautiful than that morning. If Douglas had been there personally, he would have kissed her on the cheek. Instead, he wept. Not a single tear, but gushing, giant ones. He tried not to snivel. Not that the tears would have concerned him in any way. He was a man now and mature men weep, hot liquid from the eyes. For too many years he had successfully navigated his life without crying, in sadness or in joy. However, he did want to thank Annabel without sounding like a blubbering idiot. He slowed his breathing, but couldn't contain his exuberant relief.

"I don't know how to thank you. Thank you, thank you, so much, I don't know what to say. You're an angel." Douglas gulped and sighed.

"You're most welcome. Have a wonderful trip."

Douglas dropped to his knees in the darkness. Gratitude poured out into the dawn. The Governor had pardoned the prisoner. He collapsed into a deep sleep. It was the sleep of a free man.

The wind chime ringtone of the iPhone barely stirred Douglas. The volume gradually increased. Some mornings Douglas slept through the alarm. Other mornings he slapped it. Most mornings he snoozed. This morning it was his best friend. Two hours of sleep felt like eight. He woke to a choir in the trees.

John's fingertips lightly tapped the steering wheel. He mentally prepared himself to hear the bad news. How will I explain it? I'm so sorry we couldn't get the passports. There was a problem at the Embassy. We can always try again in the Spring. None of these excuses satisfied John.

The drone of the Cadillac Escalade's engine was drowned out by a singing Englishman.

Happy days are here again.

The skies above are clear again,

So, let's sing a song of cheer again,

Happy times!

Happy nights!

Happy days!

Are here again!

When Douglas was really happy the rest of the street knew.

Douglas swung open the door and sprang up into the leather seat of the Escalade.

"They're arriving this morning!"

John, still tapping, looked incredulous while at the same time, knowing there could only be one reason for his friend's uninhibited burst of song.

"The passports? How? Last night you said there was no way we could get them. In fact, you said it was impossible.

Words came thick and fast, often in short bursts of exuberant phrases, and punctuated with exclamations like 'incredible' or 'unbelievable.' The drumming on the steering wheel stopped. John raised his cymbal to meet Douglas's. A clashing high-five climax, the end of a great overture. John had left his house ready for a requiem. Now, it had become an Ode to Joy.

Annabel had saved the day. She had also saved Douglas.

Christmas had come early. The 'boys' eagerly awaited Santa's appearance disguised as a FedEx courier. Across the street, from the HOW office, a FedEx van pulled up and began to unload the precious cargo. He never looked at the HOW offices. He distributed packages to seemingly every shop, office, bank, travel agency and restaurant on the entire street. And then, he drove away. Santa had skipped HOW.

One hour later another FedEx 'sleigh' arrived on the scene. The van crept down the block toward the HOW office, in this city of ornate Spanish Architecture, building addresses are often random and inconspicuous. The package bore an odd number. The delivery would be on the right side of the street. His eyes landed on two men waving their arms and yelling from a balcony above an Italian Restaurant. Douglas flew down the stairs four or five steps at a time. It didn't matter that his body was 64 years old. Christmas had arrived.

The driver had only one gift in his bag. He got it out and Douglas scribbled in the appropriate box. It was the fastest signature he had ever written, and almost illegible. Douglas tore open the package like a five-year-old on Christmas morning. Minutes later, John saluted as Douglas held up each passport with a look-what-I-got expression. To be sure, they inspected each one again. They were all present and accounted for. To top it off, Brian sent a text from Cal Poly to say that Chris, who had been experiencing his own living passport and visa hell, had now received his documents for India. It may have been the eleventh hour and fifty-ninth minute, but everything was now in place.

On Saturday, six hours before departure, the India-bound party gathered at the MAD Academy. Samsun's father, Steve, had organized a convoy of vehicles to take passengers and luggage from Santa Barbara to Los Angeles International Airport. Two hours later the caravan reached the Bradley International Terminal. The white striped loading zones don't accommodate lengthy goodbyes. Trolleys were grabbed, bags were loaded, and the pilgrims were quickly embraced and bid a final farewell. Now, it was on to check-in and security.

Regardless of the hassles involved, Douglas loved arranging travel. The size of the group plus cash flow issues had made this a greater challenge, although it certainly had got the adrenaline pumping. John was chatting with some of the MAD students. Douglas could almost feel the buzz generated in those conversations. He wandered over to a vacant gate where all the passengers had just been swallowed up into the walkway and their imminent departure. Douglas could see the Emirate Airbus A380-800 aircraft through the terminal window. He looked down at his boarding pass. He recalled the raised eyebrows when he had shared the name of the airlines they would be traveling on. His face displayed a rather mischievous grin. If they only knew that they will be treated like princes and princesses!

Cocooned in this quiet space, Douglas took a few minutes to savor the prospect of meeting Florencia for the first time. He reminded himself that this mission was not really about HOW, MAD or Cal Poly. Yes, they had a part in the play. But, the leading actress was Florencia. This was her story, and the courage she exhibited to come this far would support her nomination for an Academy Award. This wasn't the first time Douglas had dozed off in a movie.

The loudspeaker abruptly interrupted the sleeping Englishman. "We are now pre-boarding Emirates flight 216 to Dubai continuing on to Delhi."

At Dubai, security was tight, to say the least. Anything suspicious was rejected, re-inspected and in some cases, even dismantled or discarded.

The $4,000 professional video camera on loan from Samy's Camera of Santa Barbara made it through without a hitch. A metal black box measuring 10" by 12" was not so fortunate. The X-ray machine scanned the contents. The conveyor belt stopped and reversed. The technician leaned in, squinted, and saw the outline of two small objects. Passengers were diverted to alternate lines. The supervisor barked out an order in Arabic to his subordinates.

The black case was gently transferred to the 'operating' table. Two surgical gloves were stretched onto probes of flesh. The inspector wiped beads of sweat from his furrowed brow. He looked down at the black box. The gloves released the clasps to reveal the contents. Two devices sat still in their foam compartments ready to be activated. Walkie talkies. It was widely known that these types of devices were used by terrorists to set off bombs.

Ben and Brett were no longer casual tourists. They were now in the category of the usual suspects. It was not comfortable or comforting.

An olive-skinned man walked purposely toward the security area. John observed his newly shined black patent shoes, European cut Armani suit, wavy black hair, and Rhett Butler-like mustache.

The official set his gaze on John and Douglas and asked, "Who's in charge here?"

"We are. What's the problem?"

His tone matched his serious face. "We cannot have these devices in the aircraft cabin."

Douglas was about to say, We've just had these walkie talkies on a ten-hour flight from LAX. He held his tongue. Then his mind went to work. Florencia is already on her way. We can't afford to miss meeting her at Jaipur airport.

He put on his best face. "What do we need to do?"

The official smiled. "You might just make your connection if you follow my instructions."

He directed Douglas to carry the metal black box through immigration control, customs control, and then the ticketing counter. There it would be wrapped, checked, and rushed to the plane. Douglas took the box from Clark Gable and headed straight to Immigration control. He found himself in an alternative reality rather like Neo, leaving the natural world and entering the Matrix. Douglas picked the shortest line at Immigration. As is often the case with checkouts at a supermarket, his line took longer than all the other ones combined.

At customs, with one lone box in his hand, the officer had more interest in Douglas's container than a family of six whose children could barely be seen over the trolley tower of suitcases and carry-ons. Like a typical male, Douglas pressed the elevator button five times in rapid succession. No matter how gently or firmly he pushed nothing happened. He was certain Jesus would come back before it would arrive. Perhaps, Mohammed would make an appearance. The stairs proved to be the best escape. He ascended with the determination of a climber moving up the Hillary Step to the summit of Everest. Gasping for breath, he only wished he was carrying supplemental oxygen.

Douglas came to a long shiny silver metal counter connected to a conveyor belt. There was also a chute at the end. The opening was covered with black rubber vertical blinds. On the table was a cellophane dispenser. Tonight, at 1:00 am, it was 'self-serve.' It, however, came at a cost. The machine required 200 Dirham to dispense the cellophane.

This began a hunt for an ATM. Strange how these cash cows dot the landscape except in an emergency. It was like desperately needing to pee and the bathroom is on the other side of the airport. While sprinting like Usain Bolt through the terminal he heard an announcement, "Final call for Emirates flight 512. Passengers, please report at once to Gate A21." With only minutes to spare, he located an ATM, the 200 Dirham, bought the wrapping, addressed the package, and was assured by the flight attendant that the two walkie talkies would be on board.

Crisis averted. Now, he himself needed to make the flight. He made his way back to Terminal 3, through Immigration. At Security, he was so glad his pockets were empty and his shoes slipped on and off easily.

He didn't bother to tie the laces. One of the white-gloved men gave Douglas a congratulatory clap of the hands. Douglas thought it was worthy of an Olympic Gold medal. Breathing heavily, the amateur courier applied the brakes as soon as he clapped eyes on the team showing their boarding passes at the gate. He regained some composure after a few deeper breaths. He was also happy to hear many of the students had been declaring that the flight to Dubai 'was like Business Class,' and 'the service was outstanding.' Douglas raised his eyebrows, nodded in agreement, as he threw his backpack up into the overhead compartment. John noticed the darkened, drenched patch under Douglas' armpit. Douglas noticed John's wry smile and countered this 'odor policeman' by pulling a stick deodorant out of his toiletry bag and applying it generously.

For those members of the team for whom this was their first visit to India, landing at Indira Gandhi International in the early hours of the morning was eye-popping. One thing that fell into place as planned was meeting Dom at the airport. His flight from Madrid had been on time and comfortable enough to get a few hours' sleep. Douglas and John had tried to buy tickets for the train from Delhi to Jaipur, but to no avail. They did know from their investigation the Jaipur train was scheduled to depart from Delhi at 7:00 am.

It's doubtful whether one ever gets used to driving on any road in India. When the traffic is in full flow it's like a noisy video game where unexpected 'visitors' cross your path, at speed and without warning. To be truthful, there can be a warning, but it's often too late.

India is known for its number of deities. At last count, there were 300 million personal gods. Apparently, they are all asleep when it comes to road safety. If the team had any Catholics among them, the drive from Delhi airport to the main train station would have found them invoking the Trinity, the Blessed Virgin, St. Christopher and even, St Jude. As one student later said, he didn't know which was worse: 'not being able to see anything, or being able to see everything.'

Chapter 17

Derailed in Delhi

In India, driving a car is a war. And in a war, you don't tell
your enemy your next move. That's why no one here uses indicators!

~A former Tuk-ṭuk driver

John took over as the 'Designated Driver' and 'Tour Organizer' at this
point of the journey.

He was responsible for getting the entire team to Jaipur by 5:00 pm
Sunday afternoon. There they could check in to their hotel and, if the
showers were good, wash off the odors and grime of the journey. They had
no time to waste. They were due at Jaipur Airport by 7:45 pm. Florencia
and her three chaperones were scheduled to land at 8:20 pm. So, it was
imperative that the team HAD to catch the 7:00 am train at the New Delhi
Railway Station. With the group waiting, John walked briskly to the 'Pre-Paid
Taxi' counter.

Two young Indian men were sipping their chai when John approached.
"New Delhi Railway Station, please. I have 12 passengers."

Almost in unison, the men responded, "No problem. We give you best price." In no time bags were loaded in three taxis and the race to the train station had begun.

It was 5:30 am and a light rain began to drizzle as the three taxis merged into the fast moving Delhi traffic. The streets were already bustling with taxis, Tuk-tuks, and motorcycles. The train station was just twenty minutes away. The look on John's face was one of sheer delight. The flights had been great. The team was rested. Florencia was arriving in the evening. And, he'd seen the videos of the Delhi-Jaipur train excursion, and it included great food and captivating views of the sprawling countryside. It couldn't be more perfect. There was a small, fleeting thought in the recesses of his mind. You should have tried a little harder to get tickets before leaving. He instantly crushed such a ludicrous notion.

About a half a mile from the station, John noticed the myriad of brake lights blinking and then turning solid red. A hodgepodge of 'vehicles' and animals had quite suddenly ground to a screeching halt. Horns blared, and cows 'mooed.' Drivers got out of their 'Tuk-tuks' and assorted buses. The stadium of heavy metal bands was now circular mayhem, a kind of roundabout. Only there was no roundabout. Did anybody know where they were going? People were shouting and waving their arms, while the passengers were either laughing (if they had been to India before) or in sheet-white fear (if they were first timers). Douglas remarked it looked like scrum (a rugby term) without a ball or a quarterback sneak in American football. In either case, bodies piling on one another and complete mayhem. Only this was a rather more dangerous sport.

John observed the chaotic gridlock. "If we sit here any longer we're going to miss the train!" Through the dim light and misty morning air, he could make out a blue sign on the top of a two story building beckoning would-be travelers in India Sanskrit 'New Delhi' Railway Station.

John leapt out of his taxi. He banged on the windows of the other two vehicles. "Let's go. Get your bags!" Twelve overnight suitcases came to attention with handles up and ready to go. John motioned the team to follow him. The bleary-eyed travelers scattered into the train station parking lot and fell in line behind their leader.

"Where do I get tickets to Jaipur for the 7:00 am train?" He asked a turbaned, bearded, man sitting in a Lotus position on the wall in front of the station.

"No American tickets here! Two Kilometers. American ticket counter."

The diminutive Indian man pointed away from the station.

John was incredulous. "What? No tickets at a train station? You got to be kidding me!" This was not what John had expected.

With no apology or explanation, John barked out the order "Get in the taxis, they'll take us to get tickets!"

John now moved to the front of the taxi. He was no longer a passenger. He was commandeering this ship. The driver spoke no English, but it didn't matter. John assassinated the negative voices that were trying to invade his mind. Does he know where he's going? How do we know these are legitimate taxi drivers? What if they take us off somewhere and we're never seen again? What would the parents think if they knew what was going on? Among the other passengers, these negative thoughts took up residence.

It was 4:30 pm back in Santa Barbara. The sun was just beginning to crest over the horizon. Ella's mom was busy in the kitchen preparing a dinner for her family minus Ella. Her cell phone sat quietly on the dining table. It then vibrated once. And again.

> 'Hi mom. Arrived in Delhi.
> Can't get train tickets.
> Driving to some place to find tickets.
> Scared.'

The taxis careened and wound their way through the narrow back roads of Delhi. At what seemed like the third turn, John looked around to check that the other taxis were behind them. They were nowhere in sight.

Hell! For a second, the CEO lost his composure. He regained it. He would have to hope the other two drivers knew where they were going.

John's taxi pulled up to what appeared to be a café. Some locals were milling around outside. There was no sign of the other taxis. He looked to the left and then to the right. He then looked down the street. In the distance, two lights appeared and then came closer. He recognized the occupants. Moments later, from an entirely different direction, the last taxi arrived. John was relieved. It felt like his lost children had returned home. In his best CEO persona, and taking a leaf out of Steven Covey's *The 7 Habits of Highly Effective People,* John made light of the situation, "Welcome to India!" There were some nervous smiles.

Three 'Sherpas' directed John through an office, up some stairs, and into a back room where a man was sitting behind a computer staring at his screen.

"You look for tickets?"

"Yes, we need to get on the 7:00 am train to Jaipur."

The man looked up at the clock. It read 6:50 am.

"I think not."

"I can get you on a 4:30 pm train."

John moved closer to the desk. "That won't work. We have to be in Jaipur at that time."

The man calmly opened his drawer and pulled out a card and handed it to John. On the card in the upper left-hand corner was a name - 'R. Suri.' In the middle of the card it read, 'Experience India; Complete Travel Planner, Car Rental, Hotel Booking, Package Tour.'

John was not about to get into another taxi. He called the number. "R. Suri Speaking. May I help you?"

"Mr. Suri, this is John Mullen, I have twelve people that need passage to Jaipur."

"No problem, Mr. Mullen. I have a bus leaving at 8:00 am for Jaipur. Come to my office across from the train station and we'll take care of you."

John was still in a vigilante mindset as the taxis now headed back to the train station. He was a shepherd herding his sheep back into the pen. We could still make it if this travel agent actually has a bus.

The team was now back in familiar territory. The train station was somewhat less foreboding than it had been in the pre-dawn hours. The sun was rising in the Indian sky with hues of brown, yellow, and orange. John saw the sign way before they arrived. It was a beautiful sight to behold. 'Experience India Travel Tours.' John ran into the office to meet his new best friend and potential savior, R. Suri.

"Mr. Mullen, I've been looking forward to your arrival. Please take a seat. I have a bus coming in a few minutes. I said I would take care of you. The bus will arrive in Jaipur this afternoon." Mr. Siri sounded very confident.

On the drive to meet R. Suri, John had time to reflect.

A bus could mean a lot of things in India — he had firsthand experience. Everything from a bus with no truck windows to ones more suited for animals. Some buses did sound and smell like a farm on wheels. And what if this is a salvage bus from one of those buses that I saw lying on its side.

With these sobering insights, John clarified with Mr. Suri just what kind of bus they could expect.

"Oh, Mr. Mullen this is excellent bus and travels to Jaipur often. It will be very comfortable."

John thought, *even a school bus would work…at least we're going to Jaipur.*

Chapter 18

In the Pink

Initially, you're overwhelmed. But gradually you realize it's like a wave.
Resist, and you'll be knocked over. Dive into it, and you'll swim out the other side.

~Evelyn (Dame Judi Dench) "The Best Exotic Marigold Hotel"

The particle-filled polluted Delhi air had made John's throat desperate for a bottle of water. He also realized that he no idea if they would stop on the way to Jaipur.

A few doors down from R. Suri's office John eyed a shop that was open. He bought bottled water for everyone. True to the agent's promise a very clean, respectable bus arrived. The fifty passenger bus had one or two passengers already seated. John counted his group, in case the chocolate in the store had proved too much of a temptation for one of the MAD students. No, they were all smiling and ready for the road trip. The CEO sank into his seat and pressed the button at the end of the armrest. The seat responded to the slight pressure from John's back. Whoa! Not only soft seats, recliners. *A job well done.*

A few rows back Ella's fast thumbs punched the keys on the tiny screen.

We are on the bus to Jaipur.
All is good. Love you, mom!

Ella smiled. Thousands of miles away, her mom and dad also smiled.

Some movie lovers will recall the perils of this particular journey. The scene is from *The Best Exotic Marigold Hotel*, a story of some aging seniors from Britain traveling to Jaipur to check out if retiring to India might be something worth thinking about. They too travel the road from Delhi to Jaipur and 'enjoy' the ride of their lives. Well, more like survive! Some characters think it might be their final journey. The phrase 'an accident waiting to happen,' was probably created on just such a road.

Douglas remarked to John that he had seen the movie in a spectacular boutique theatre, (you get to drink wine while watching the movie in luxury armchairs). Dorothy Browns in Arrowtown, New Zealand is a cut above the norm of places to see a movie, and if the movie is of a high quality, it is a memorable evening of entertainment. Douglas and Fiona were with their good friend, Gill Hodgson. How they laughed and sighed at the sight of these Brits who were old enough to remember the days of the Raj and Empire. Laughter really is good for the soul. And when there are two legends of the cinema in the cast, Dame Judi Dench and Dame Maggie Smith, you know one is in for a rare treat.

Staring into a contemplative space, almost oblivious of the vendors at the side of the road and his colleagues in the bus, Douglas was transported to a place he had never been, Macachula, Mozambique. On the screen of his inner eye, he could see Florencia's home. A matchbox hut with a thatched roof. Guilda was sitting with her grandson, Guildo. Florencia stood leaning on her broken crutch washing large metal saucepans. By now, the eighteen-year-old had made herself an accomplished crutch user. There were odd moments when, if somebody said something funny, she would offer a coy smile. But, much of the time a dark cloud of sadness hung over her. It showed. A young mother able to do the practical things, but not the truly meaningful ones – sit on a mat with Guildo, then lift him, and get up together, all in one swift movement. When Guildo found something, while playing, he couldn't take his mom by the hand and pull her to see his startling discovery, even if it was, merely a worm.

Tonight, Florencia would land in Jaipur. He hoped the travel would go well. Thank God Victoria was able to come as well. Aderito was marvelous. But sometimes only a woman can help another woman.

Douglas couldn't wait to finally meet Florencia in the flesh and shake the hands of his friend, Aderito.

The whole episode faded as Samsun nudged Douglas. The bus slowed down and pulled off to the side of the road onto a dirt patch. No sooner had the door of the bus opened than the rich aroma of Indian spices and cooking wafted into the bus.

The outdoor diner fused the architectural design elements of corrugated metal, plastic, and wood. A huge flat cooking grill lined the rear wall where a cook was rolling out the traditional naan bread. Some of the team described it as an Indian 'Hole in the wall' place where the food was ordered and eaten on the large tables outside. Adjacent to the 'restaurant' was a kiosk that was the equivalent of an Indian version of a 7-Eleven.

Douglas ordered the food. He did try to make it clear to the man taking the order, that not everyone would jump at the chance to taste their spiciest version of curried chicken. In other words, while Douglas would have been delighted to taste the 'vindaloo' (the hottest and spiciest flavor) he was pretty confident not too many of the others would want to join him on the gastronomic adventure. Once again, John was impressed with the willingness of everyone on the team to at least attempt to eat what was set in front of them. The kiosk came in very handy. Douglas declined the man's offer of free water. He knew it wasn't really free. Those who drank it would pay a high price later. Everyone stuck to the ever-reliable Coke and Sprite.

The bus dropped the enlivened visitors at the outskirts of Jaipur, known as the Pink City, a testimony to the colorful walls and buildings.

Not everything is pink, but the many Palaces, Temples and Fortified Walls are all distinguished and bold. Amber and red combine with the pink to make this a must-see tourist city. Cameras need to be unlocked and ready for action. Elephants, monkeys and snake charmers abound. Ben and Brett and the MAD guys were clicking faster than the Beijing bullet train. No film to load or unload. Already the millennial generation are asking, 'what does loading a film mean?' Unless you are one of the ancient ones or compelled to do a History of Photography class why would you know? And if you hate the shot? Hit the delete button when you get home. It's gone, erased and at no cost. Photography paradise. Picture not quite perfect? No problem, Photoshop will take care of it, or even, create an entirely different backdrop. It's shoot, shoot, and then, shoot some more. Ok, not for the real pros, but, for the mere mortals, this is all it takes.

Jaipur is one corner of a triangle of cities that are on the checklist of any visitor to North India. The other two corners cities, some few hundred kilometers away, are Delhi and Agra. Agra is home to India's most historic landmark building, the Taj Mahal. Instantly recognizable, the Taj is immense and magnificent. Yet she possesses a romantic charm that is a magnet that draws thousands of admirers every day. From the very first glimpse to the last look before leaving, the pilgrim is in stunned awe.

India is one of those places that provides an endless supply of material for storytellers, especially in describing the bizarre and strange modes of transportation. At the heart of most narratives is the infamous 'Tuk- tuk.' The Tuk-tuk is India's version of the taxi cab. It has been aptly described by Cam and Nicole Wears, a Canadian couple who write a blog on international travel, as a 'lawnmower with a rusty metal bubble on top.' This three-wheeled bag of bolts provides a roller-coaster ride for the daring, or more appropriately, naïve, occupants.

John hailed three Tuk-tuks to take the team the rest of the way to their hotel-cum-guest house. Tuk-tuk drivers have no set price for their fare. They do expect and invite haggling. It's one of their national pastimes. They began asking 500 rupees per vehicle, which is about $10 US dollars.

John, the adroit negotiator pretended to walk away two times. The price moved lower and eventually was cut in half. While bartering for a price, he learned an important cultural feature in the art of negotiation. In America, we shake our head to the right and left to signify 'no.' In India, it's the exact opposite. John called it 'head bobbing.' 'Yes,' is communicated by moving the head back and forth much like the 'infinity' sign. With an affirmative head bobbing, John said, "Ok. Let's go to the hotel." Little did he know what lay ahead on the road to Jaipur. The team loaded luggage and camera gear to the brim and got on board.

Tuk-tuk drivers don't display any 'taxi' license and there's no evidence by their reckless driving that they've ever been required by the government to pass a road test. To say they're superstitious would be an understatement. Hanging from the rear view mirror of each Tuk-tuks are multi-colored prayer garlands, charms to ward off the 'accident' spirit, and a row of worn and tattered pictures of their family.

The only way to describe the thumping sound the engine emits would be its likeness to the motorcars at the Autobahn Raceway at Disneyland. Put-put...put-put...put-put. This ride, however, would not under any circumstances qualify as the 'happiest place on earth.' The driver squeezes and revs his motorcycle throttle. The engine wakes up. It hacks out a cough and then another. The put-put...put-put increases in tempo and the wheels begin to slowly spin as it advances onto the roadway. Joining the snarl of traffic, the Tuk-tuk's gain speed and fight for space. One barely misses a cow, another shifts to avoid an oncoming vehicle, and almost tips over. A pedestrian leaps to safety. Nobody apparently has the right of way. In this vehicular jungle, operable horns are not optional but a necessity for survival. The shrill 'beep, beep' keep danger at bay.

As the caravan made their way into the heart of Jaipur, it didn't take long to discover that the drivers had no clue where they were going, and neither did most of the people they asked to direct them. No onboard GPS system. This is where westerners are often fooled by a kind of cultural phenomena. The lovely Indian people so want to please others that the idea of saying, 'I don't know,' is the farthest thing from their mind. Then there is the person who actually does know exactly where the place is and opens up, 'Sorry, you cannot get there from here.' Eventually, (ah, the very word covers a multitude of stoppages, dead ends, and breaks for drinks) the team arrived at the Goyal Haveli.

Rishu and Poovra, a brother and sister team management at the Goyal Haveli. went out of their way to facilitate the team's rooms. Not the luxury of decadence, but the team could have a whole floor to themselves. Rishu had a talent that belongs to most Indians. He was a good negotiator, but he was also very kind. Douglas and John worked out a win-win deal (aka Steven Covey style), for guests and the manager.

Much of India had grown up in the twenty-two years since Douglas had first explored this abject poverty and squalor. Now there are airports with marble flooring on which you could eat your lunch, Hospitals that surpass many four star hotels in the West, and have surgeons and researchers at the fresh frontiers of health solutions. And these solutions come at a tenth of the cost for the same in America.

Once the rooms were sorted and some light snacks eaten there was a noted rise in the level of anticipation. The wait was almost over. Florencia and her three chaperones, Aderito, Victoria and Stephane, would land at 8:20 am at Jaipur airport.

The ride to the airport was cramped, but it was a short one. Whether it was the fatigue from the travel and dreams of their first hours in India the drive was rather more subdued than on the bus. Maybe, they were dwelling on the reason why they had all come these thousands of miles, and the arrival of Florencia.

The security that has changed air travel for the whole world since the attack on the World Trade Center was in evidence at Jaipur airport. The camera crews were made to position themselves outside the terminal. John and Douglas did manage to gain entry by paying for a special ticket. A man and a woman, in uniform and each armed with a serious looking weapon, were watching their every move. Any step to approach the area where the Mozambicans would emerge was countered with a stern look from the two guards. John and

Douglas had done an awful lot of waiting in the last six months, but somehow this seemed longer. The clock appeared to move slower and slower.

Then Aderito appeared in the distance, pushing a trolley of luggage, John and Douglas recognized Florencia. She was in a wheelchair. Victoria and Stephane walked alongside. Cameras were at the ready. From behind the glass window, the faces of all the team were lit up by the scene before them. Handshakes and hugs signaled not just the joy of meeting for the first time, but the sense that this was a very special moment.

Everyone gathered around Florencia. They all knew that this encounter would live with them for the rest of their lives. Florencia looked shy, somewhat sad, but mainly, overwhelmed. The airport wheelchair was abandoned. The old ill-fitting crutches slotted into their usual place, held tightly by strong hands.

It was Florencia's only way of getting around. Not for much longer.

Part 3

GOODNESS BLOOMS

Chapter 19

A Prince of Grace

Grace finds beauty in ugly things.

~Bono

They crawl like spiders. Some fast. Some slow. You wouldn't think they were God's creatures. Broken. In need of repair. The dregs of society.

Thousands of miles away, in magnificent buildings well-dressed people stand and sing:

> All things bright and beautiful,
> All creatures great and small,
> All things wise and wonderful,
> The Lord God made them all.
>
> He gave us eyes to see them,
> And lips that we might tell,
> How great is God Almighty,
> Who has made all things well.

The sight of these creatures here would silence the song, or at least make it difficult to sing with the same gusto.

They shuffle on their haunches. Buttocks barely off the ground. Others manage to move with one good leg and a long stick, like Long

John Silver in Treasure Island. Only this isn't a movie.

A few have two modern crutches. Don't be thinking these are the lucky ones. They are not. They've had their leg cut off.

The ultimate tragedy is those who have no legs at all. Like a crab exiled on a sandy beach left to claw its way home.

Welcome to Jaipur Foot…

Almost 140 years ago, an Irish novelist, Margaret Wolfe Hungerford, wrote a romantic novel, Molly Bawn. It is still in print today. Contained in the 480 pages of this book is one revealing thought. It's a truth that is over two thousand years old. Margaret penned the idea in these eight memorable words, 'Beauty is in the eye of the beholder.' When she published the book, she could never have known that this phrase would, eventually, become a cliché. Today, most writers would avoid its use. It's rather stale and hackneyed. However, Jaipur Foot infuses these eight words with a fresh and profound application.

Through the lens of an architect, the structure that houses this clinic is plain. For this beholder, beauty is a word that will not enter the architect's mind or mouth, and never find its way into a report. His conclusions would express the obvious; Commercial, Storefront, Aluminum swing doors, dull, gray concrete slab floors, high ceilings, faded white plastered walls, simple décor, rows of tandem black sling chairs, and basic flickering fluorescent tubes. Not many architects come to Jaipur Foot. It is of little interest to them.

But, if this same architect loses his leg in a car accident, or to diabetes, he will be recognized as an amputee much more than he is an architect, both in his eyes, and those around him.

From the moment he lost his leg he's had to change his view of the playing field of life. He discovers a whole new world that had been hidden in plain view. Colleagues, neighbors and friends find it hard to relate. There are periods where he is overwhelmed with self-consciousness, even shame. He has kept his job but it has become difficult in the extreme. Clients look away and coworkers can be heard to utter, "It's such a pity." Slowly, he succumbs to the temptation to socially withdraw. He's fortunate to be able to work, but it yields little comfort. Depression closes the channels of appreciation and gratitude. He walks with his crutches but he also throws them down in anger and disgust. *Nobody understands what I'm going through.*

Then he crutches into that courtyard space and sees people where, before he had only seen the cement. *How did I miss these people? They were invisible to me the last time I came.*

He enters through the doors without a thought as to their lack of distinction or creative design. Invariably, the welcome is warm and embracing. So kind, that the architect almost forgets he is an amputee. At every stage of the process, the old self-consciousness slips away and the chips of shame are chiseled from each shoulder. With successive conversations, the crusty, inner, angst of isolation is softened. Each healing touch on his tender stump is so natural and fearless. His saving device is hand crafted and fitted with devotion. The therapy is assertive yet encouraging. He departs through the same doors, but a new and different man. Walking. Dignity is restored and a fresh view of life on offer.

This is the most beautiful place on earth.

The ones who crawl, hop, and limp, have not come to this clinic to admire the building. For these pilgrims, Jaipur Clinic offers a practical solution to their dire need. For most, it's their last hope. They have traveled here because of word-of-mouth stories. Tales of people who limped in and walked out. A polio victim from Kathmandu comes for calipers, a motor accident amputee arrives from Madurai in the deep south to receive a prosthetic, a father from Bengaluru brings his young son who has outgrown his artificial limb and needs a replacement. Hope here is not cheap. It's free.

The green and yellow Tuk-tuk rounded the corner into the Jaipur Foot Clinic courtyard. The driver killed the engine. Petrol is a precious commodity. John and Douglas emerged into the throng. Some of the people clamored for the few rupees that might feed their empty stomachs. In this place the disabled are comfortable and the abled distinctly uncomfortable. They slowly moved up the marble stairs. John turned his head and centered his gaze. He was aghast. Standing before him was a statue. But it wasn't DR Mehta, a great benefactor, or even a member of parliament. Instead, what stood before him was an emaciated one-legged man on crutches. Why on earth would they put that figure in front of this clinic? It makes no sense. He glanced back at the figures in the courtyard. It was an 'aha' moment. Actually, it proved to be an epiphany to John. The statue revealed the true MVP's (Most Valuable People) of this clinic.

John and Douglas wound their way through the building to a rear courtyard. Prakash Bhandari, DR Mehta's assistant greeted them with the news that Mehta would be delayed a few minutes. DR Mehta's office is a space of which Mother Teresa would be proud, and in which Mahatma Gandhi would be comfortable. John surveyed the space. It was the second eye-opener of the day. This is about the size of one of my walk-in closets without the space to walk! Douglas would later remark to John that Mehta's office reminded him of a visit to a monastery. There the monk's bedroom was Spartan.

Two desks sit side by side. Mehta's desk is the smaller and could be found at any Goodwill store. The desk next to him is occupied by Prakash Bhandari. Along the opposite side is a row of chairs and a bench seat for guests whether it be a dignitary from India, an ambassador from another country, two writers on a humanitarian mission, a MAD high school student, a Cal Poly senior engineer, or a patient freshly fitted with a new prosthetic. Lining the back wall are scores of awards by governments, educational institutions, corporations, and non-profit organizations for Jaipur's Foot's humanitarian work across the globe. At the end of the room high on the wall is the only sign of technology. A large screen monitor for viewing emails and letters transcribed by Mr. Bhandari for DR Mehta.

It is on this large screen the words were scribed to HOW to bring a young 18-year-old Mozambique amputee, living in the Bush, to come to Jaipur to be fitted with a prosthetic leg. It would also be on this screen that a Memorandum of Understanding between Jaipur Foot and HOW would be drafted to bring legs to the 10,000 landmine victims of Mozambique.

One may have surmised that DR Mehta is not your typical executive. He doesn't carry a briefcase. He takes no salary for his ten-hour plus work days. He doesn't even have an expense account. In fact, he proudly provides his own water bottles at no cost to Jaipur Foot. Unlike most CEO's he doesn't spend his days devising strategies and policies to improve the bottom line. Mehta defines bottom line in a radically different way. For him, it's not about how many rupees or dollars are earned. It's about how many legs are given away.

DR Mehta walked into his office with a former Minister of Health of Pakistan and a senior official with the Social Work Department of Bangladesh. There is a sudden realization this is the fellowship of the caring. There are people that advertise one persona in emails and then quite another in person. In this instance, DR Mehta proved to be one of the most authentic and compassionate people they had ever come across. To John and Douglas, this was a truly historic moment.

In the middle of the meeting, Mehta took a phone call and asked to be excused for a few minutes. In the interim, John and Douglas exchanged stories with his honored guests. The woman from Bangladesh was planning a prosthetic camp in her country and John and Douglas shared their desire to do the same in Mozambique. When Mehta returned, he conveyed that he was saying goodbye to an amputee who was returning home after receiving a first prosthetic. It was striking to see Mehta leave dignitaries with two visitors from California while he tended to one of the 'least of these.'

If Rudyard Kipling were around today, back in the country of his birth, and met Mehta, he would immediately be reminded of a number of lines from his poem 'If', but these two in particular,

> If you can walk crowds and keep your virtue,
> Or walk with kings - nor lose the common touch.

He has the capacity to look beyond the externals; to live from the heart. This is what it means to walk in grace. This transforms what one sees in the natural, and allows the inner eye to see a hidden beauty. It is the artistry of grace.

The discernment of love. It enables others. It is mysteriously simple, yet extraordinarily difficult. You don't learn it from a textbook or a seminar. There are no (pick a number) 5 steps to grace or 4 steps to love as some would like us to believe. This cocktail of grace is mixed from a variety of ingredients and most who provide the drink of kindness will tell you it didn't come easy for them.

Bono taps into this phenomenon in his powerful 'hymn' to Grace. It could be the anthem of DR Mehta and Jaipur Foot, written on the walls and lived out in their work, from the cleaners to the technicians and the administrators to the doctors. The provision of prosthetics for the least and the great renders the two categories meaningless. In the House of Jaipur, this practical love is extended to all, and dignity is restored to all.

She carries a pearl
In perfect condition
What once was hurt
What once was friction
What left a mark
No longer stings

Because grace makes beauty
Out of ugly things

Grace finds beauty
In everything,
Grace finds goodness in everything

Bono reminds all of humanity…Grace
It's also a thought that Changed the world.

Chapter 20

Namasté
(Nah-mah-stay)

Nobody is superior, nobody is inferior, but nobody is equal either.
People are simply unique, incomparable.

~ Osho

The Tuk-tuk drivers left the hotel with Aderito and Florencia seated and holding on to the metal sides. The MAD guys and Culture Spark had left earlier to set up what would be a key scene in the short documentary.

Once at Jaipur Clinic, the crews positioned themselves to take a variety of video and stills of Florencia arriving. It was fascinating to the media crew that India is one of those countries where the people love being photographed, regardless of limb loss or poverty. It was an unexpected bonus. The subject of the portraits saw themselves immediately, instantly, and it brought huge grins and a lot of laughter.

Aderito helped Florencia alight from their Tuk-tuk. She looked around. For Jaipur it was quite normal, but for this shy and rather apprehensive young woman, far from home, it was a revelation. She grabbed her crutches and stood, staring. There was what might be called a pregnant pause. How would this affect her? Aderito speculated. No longer was she the odd person in her village at Macachula. In this little 'village' within the city of Jaipur, there were not only many like her, there were others whose condition was far worse. Aderito sensed some tension broke at Florencia's sight of the other patients. Aderito picked up Florencia's bag and slotted in behind her. The doors opened and the cameras clicked.

Dane and the rest of the MAD team were shooting footage of Florencia as well as many snapshots of the workers and visitors to the clinic. Florencia spent much of the day undergoing tests on her health in general. But, most of the attention was given to her amputated right leg. Measurements were taken so the socket would be a precise and comfortable fit. It's well-nigh impossible to imagine Florencia's state of mind. She hadn't been near any doctor or clinic since the day a part of her leg was removed at the clinic in Inhambane. She also had never seen a person with a prosthetic leg.

DR Mehta found the team and shook the hand of each member. One couldn't help notice the extra special welcome he reserved for Florencia. It was as if DR was a genial grandfather meeting his own favorite granddaughter. His greeting oozed with a natural warmth and genuine charm. There was not a trace of pity in his face or words. Pure grace, and the princess from Mozambique returned the compliment with a ray of sunshine that had long since been hidden behind the dark clouds created on that fateful day.

With introductions over, everyone was surprised when DR said he would take them on a guided tour of the facility and the work being done. Process by process was described by this unique Chief Patron. Mehta explained part of the history of Jaipur Foot and the various stages in its development. One of the highlights was when a small man, who had been pacing in and out of the rooms, was asked by Mehta to sit down. The man proceeded to lift his trouser up take off his right prosthetic, only to be followed by the removal of his left one also. Florencia would later tell the people of her own village, it was this moment where she laughed. Confidence and hope, deadened by a landmine, was emerging once more. She too would walk again. She too would walk again. Dom, the only member the Cal Poly engineers present, had many questions for DR on some of the technical aspects of the prosthetic production.

It was late in the afternoon when the tea arrived back at the Goyal Haveli. It was the second time a vein of confidence had bubbled to the surface. It was Kendall, Chris, and Derek, checking in. They looked surprisingly fresh. Dom shared with them the report of the first day's activities and his conversations with DR.

Typical of his spontaneous expression of his life, DR approached John and Douglas on Wednesday, the third morning, and asked if they'd like to join him on a short site visit to a prosthetic camp. John jumped at the invitation. Partly, because Tuesday had been one tough day for Florencia and John wasn't sure he could endure another day. Douglas desired to go but knew that one of them would need to stay back because this was the same day Florencia would be fully testing out her new prosthetic.

The previous day-and-a-half Florencia had been wearing a trial prosthetic leg and attempting to walk with the support of two 'Olympic' parallel bars. Much like an Olympic trial, if the team members were holding up judges' score cards, the results weren't promising. Two out of ten for movement. Nine out of ten for determination. A dozen pair of suffering eyes could scarce believe what they were seeing. No one dared say a word. It was written on their faces. This was not what anyone had anticipated.

Florencia sat in a waiting area, outside the room where the doctors fitted her prosthetic. Still pained from the session she was slumped in her chair. She desperately needed a lift. Luke must have noticed because he sat down opposite Florencia. He pulled out a pack of playing cards and spread them on the table, in front of Florencia. She raised her head. With his best sign language, Luke managed to get Florencia to pick up a card and keep it secret. Genius. She gave him the card, making sure it was not revealed. Luke shuffled the pack. Then he started dealing the cards face up.

When the Queen of spades was dealt, he pointed at Florencia, indicating that this was the card. His pointing finger was met with guffaws of laughter from the tired Mozambican traveler. Six or seven magic tricks later Florencia was a completely different girl, waving her hand to tell Luke to do another trick. This was comic relief for Florencia and Luke's talent and joy in seeing her delight was a much needed distraction for both of them. Florencia from the attempts at walking, and Luke from coping with his mother's illness. It was a key moment of bonding for the high school team, sitting around the card table with Florencia. It was the perfect therapy and antidote for the trials of the morning.

John and Aderito stepped into a minivan with DR for a two-hour drive to Malpura, some 70 kilometers away. Another vehicle followed close behind. It was driven by Nita Daga, a close friend of DR and strong supporter of the work of the Clinic. Dan and Ella, as well as Nita's daughter, accompanied Nita on the drive. Nita lives with her husband, Rajeev, in Houston, Texas.

The team arrived at Malpura. Thankfully, the rich conversations on the way had averted their eyes from the road. John noticed, through his car window, that there was a group of about thirty people dressed colorfully as they approached an intersection in the small city. They held leis in their hands and looked like they were on their way to a birthday party or a wedding. The conversations stopped as the others realized they had reached their destination. DR Mehta stepped out and greeted those who were clearly his friends. Each person placed their palms together in a greeting and bowed to DR Mehta. John couldn't quite be sure but they said something like 'NARMARSTAY,' and it went with the hands- together- routine. Must be a prayer. He felt confident in his assessment but, if the right moment came, he'd confirm it with Mehta. It was then that DR Mehta motioned to the team to get out of the cars and one by one they were given leis and welcomed with the hands together and 'namaste' greeting. The welcome complete, the team got back into the cars. Wandering over to the vehicles John found himself strolling with Nita.

"Why are they all bowing and putting their hands together as if praying?"

Nita laughed, a good strong laugh. "It is a traditional greeting in our culture." We greet dignitaries by placing your palms together and say, 'Namaste.' It's a combination of two words, "Nama" and "Te". Nama means to 'bow' in reverence for the person and 'Te' means 'to you.' So, Namaste means 'I bow to you.'

Not too far away, thought John. *We are certainly being treated way above our status. I guess if you are friends with DR Mehta it carries a degree of reverence. It feels otherworldly. Why us? We merely came along as observers, yet, these people confer on us the highest respect.*

The next stop was lunch. The meal consisted of a Biryani, a spicy curry traditional Indian dish with vegetables, rice, Chole Bhature (spiced curried chickpeas), and Chapati, India's version of a Mexican flour tortilla was served. Once lunch was finished, these foreign 'dignitaries' were taken on a short tour of a Jain Temple. Jainism is an ancient religion formed 3000 years ago. It is well known that the word "Jain" is taken from the Sanskrit word Jina (Conqueror). To become enlightened, it requires a life of inner discipline and a conquering of passions such as greed, pride, desire, and attachment. The path to spirituality is sought through a lifestyle of asceticism and complete non-violence towards all creatures. Jain Temples are simple structures but with very elaborate statues, garnished with glass, gold, silver, and ivory. Out of respect, the participants were asked to remove their shoes and walk quietly through the rooms.

The main event was the camp and the team arrived there in the early afternoon. More ritual followed. This time, a brightly colored Turban was placed on each head as if they were arriving royalty. Then a bindi, or red dot, was placed on the forehead. This symbol is popular in Indian culture, it serves as a sign to ward off anything negative or hurtful.

The camp was set up in a commercial building and there were about 200 attendees seated. To the right of the building was what appeared to be a converted recreational vehicle. The team walked into this makeshift clinic where prosthetics were fabricated and patients fitted. Two long tables were placed in the front of a sea of chairs. The Americans and Aderito, (a.k.a. Aladdin from Mozambique) were shuffled to the front to a privileged place at the head table.

John spied a flag with an emblem, "Malpura Rotary Club.' What is the Rotary Club doing all the way out here in this small city in India?' Then he noticed badges on the leaders and he knew that this camp was sponsored by Rotary International. He discovered later the work of Rotary is renowned for its global work among amputees and polio victims.

DR Mehta rose to speak. The lively chatter ceased and was replaced by a distinct hush. He delivered his message in an Indian dialect and then translated so the guests at the head table could understand.

"We come here today to celebrate amputees receiving prosthetics, those with polio receiving bikes that can be operated with hands, and hearing aids for those who have lost their hearing. In total there had been 500 patients over a period of one month. With me today is the team from the United States. Two men discovered a 16-year-old amputee in the middle of the Bush of Eastern Africa and they have brought a team all the way to India to help her receive a prosthetic limb. I am overwhelmed that these two men would go to this effort to help one girl. We are here to honor them today."

The head table was silent. Not the same silence as the crowd listening intently to Mehta. More like they were uncomfortable and embarrassed. Nor was it the first time since reading of Florencia's tragedy in the National Geographic, John felt his eyes water and a couple of tears escaped the eyes and began to make their way down his cheeks. In fact, it was rare not to cry in the telling of her story. Aderito looked at his knees with a hint of pink in his dark complexion. It was an awkward humbling. There was nothing to say. What was profoundly strange was the immediacy of kinship, as though they were all family. This small town in India was hosting an international team to observe the caring and the needy, sponsored by a remarkable, philanthropic organization and led by a unique humanitarian from Jaipur.

This was an operation of love, led by a Friend to the least – it was another epiphany.

No longer could these four be satisfied to be defined by titles or accomplishments: CEO; Student; Director; Deminer; or any other position they might rise to in the future. One cannot be around DR Mehta for long before some accepted views and priorities are challenged, and some serious reassessments found to be in order.

David Brooks, the journalist and commentator on PBS, has shrewdly drawn a distinction relating to values. Our resume values and our eulogy values. A resume describes what we do. A eulogy alludes to who we are. Brooks notes,

'The résumé virtues are the ones you put on your résumé, which are the skills you bring to the marketplace. The eulogy virtues are the ones that get mentioned in the eulogy, which are deeper: who are you, in your depth, what is the nature of your relationships, are you bold, loving, dependable, consistent? And most of us, including me, would say that the eulogy virtues are the more important of the virtues. But at least in my case, are they the ones that I think about the most?'

These four day-trippers to a prosthetic camp in India had learned more in a few hours than many learn in years of schooling or decades of living. They had encountered a man whose values and work were in harmony.

DR Mehta had, himself, been crushed years earlier. Out of that dark and pain-wracked season has blossomed a man who exudes a quiet peace, and has tireless supplies of practical love. At the age of 79, he still helps thousands of other broken and bent VIP'S (Very Important Poor) to walk, smile and dance again.

And that is, simply, beautiful.

Chapter 21

Tragedy and Triumph

The only thing necessary for the triumph of
evil is for good men to do nothing.

~ Edmund Burke

Adrianne Haslet-Davis is a ballroom dancer from Boston. In the time it takes to read the nine words above, her bloody, left leg was hanging by little more than a sinuous thread.

Dancing, and life as she had known it, was over. Adrianne was not the only one. There were sixteen others who lost a leg. Some lost both legs. Three people were killed.

The Place? Boylston Street, Boston
The Date? April 15, 2013
The Scene? The Finish of the 117th Boston Marathon

Adrianne recalls that moment in remarkable detail, considering the shock.

"I remember everything. I remember every detail. I remember the first bomb going off and screaming and holding on to Adam and saying, 'Oh no, oh no, please no.' And I remember smelling smoke, and everyone around us just seemed very still and very quiet."

"The first one went off, I grabbed a hold of Adam. It was: 'We need to go inside. Wait, should we be outside? Maybe we should be.' And then, the second bomb went off, and it went off directly in front of us. And I remember the pressure from the air hitting my chest and my stomach, and sailing me backwards onto my left side, and landing, sort of in a pretzel with Adam. We sort of landed as we sleep, you know, just sort of curled up. I was a big spoon around him."

"And he said, 'Are you OK?' And I said, 'Yeah, I think I'm OK. I think we're OK. I can't believe it, I think we're OK.' And then a couple seconds went by, or minutes, or who knows. And then I said, 'I think my foot hurts.'
"And I said, 'Oh, my foot hurts bad. It really hurts.' And I sat up, and then, I looked at my foot the same time (was it the same time?) that Adam looked at my foot. And he picked up my foot, and it was dangling. Most of my heel was gone, and I could see my toes were still attached, but most of the bones and everything were gone.

"And he just started screaming, and I started screaming."

"I remember telling a lot of doctors that I was a ballroom dancer, and that it was extremely important that I kept my foot, that I could still feel every toe and move every toe. I rolled my foot around, what was left of it, to know that the nerves and the brain were still attached ... I woke up and I didn't have a foot anymore. I didn't have a left foot anymore."

Yet, from her hospital bed, she declared, "I will dance again."

This is the resilience of the human spirit. In Boston, that resilience became a united rallying cry, 'Boston Strong.'

While Adrianne was undergoing intensive rehabilitation, a rock-climbing professor paid her a visit. Only this was a unique rock-climber, and a very special professor. Hugh Herr is missing two legs. He is also the director of Bio-Mechatronics at Massachusetts Institute of Technology.

He spent a brief time visiting with Adrianne, offering a sympathetic hand and kind words.

While driving back to his office, the professor couldn't get Adrianne's condition out of his mind. Surely something should be done for her. After all, dancing was not only her passion, it was her career. He started to think out loud, *Wait a minute. I've got a lab, equipment and a team of creative engineers. Why don't we design her a leg? We can develop a leg so she can dance.*

The project became a mission, almost an obsession. It would need to be, if they were to succeed.

They investigated the dynamics of dance styles including; Foxtrot, Waltz, Hip-Hop, Salsa and Tango. Through computer simulation they were able to mimic the movement required for a bionic leg. She went through extensive therapy and training to learn to walk again. But walking was not enough. The months of trials and adjustments culminated in a final prosthetic. The 'dancing leg' was ready for Adrianne. But was she ready? Could she dance? Not some kind of slow motion routine that would gain sympathetic applause, but a real dance.

Two hundred days after the fateful Patriot's Day tragedy, Hugh gave a talk at a TED Conference to a packed auditorium. It was full of humor and pathos. It centered on human creativity and will power. But, Hugh's talk was more show than tell. And the 'show' came in the final three minutes.

The star of the show was none other than Adrianne Haslet-Davis. This was the first public demonstration of the dancing leg and Adrianne's spirit. Her Rumba, performed with Christian Lightner, was flawless. Christian didn't mind at all that every eye was on the brave beauty. The place erupted. Everyone stood to their feet. The rapturous applause went on and on in salute to engineering genius and human courage. But the audience couldn't see and taste those two hundred long, long days.

Those two hundred days included breakthrough days, angry days, impatient days, depressing days, setback days. And, after the applause died away, many of those days would return. Adrianne would express later it was great to dance, but it wasn't the same. How could it be? The leg on which she was born to dance, with was gone, forever.

Adrianne's triumph has been viewed by over four million people on social media. Her words define her future and embolden amputees everywhere, "I refuse to be called a victim. I am not defined by what happened in my life. I am a survivor, defined by how I live my life." Douglas watched the talk, eyes glued to his computer screen to watch Adrianne Haslet-Davis. He had a special interest. His daughter Laura had seemed all set to finish about the time the second bomb went off on that fateful Patriots Day. She was stopped immediately by a police cordon, a few hundred meters from the finish. A great sense of irony occurred to Douglas. Years before Florencia had stepped on the landmine, he had shown Hugh and Adrianne's TED Talk to more than twenty friends around the world. We never know if the incidents of our lives will become the dots that providence or chance connect down the road.

All men and women may be created equal, but not all tragedies are equal. This is not to diminish the horror and ongoing issues that Adrianne and the other Boston bombing victims have faced. These courageous people have brought the public's attention to the needs of amputees throughout the world. But, what of the victims hidden from plain view? Those who live in the jungle, the Bush, and Urban wastelands. These are the undiscovered or forgotten. Thousands of amputees in Mozambique are not even registered, and certainly not the new item in the newspapers around the globe. Perhaps that is why so little is done for them.

Unlike Boston, where a phenomenal $20 million dollars has enabled vital care and support services to provide for the victims, Mozambique amputee victims of the maiming devices lie on the ground in their villages. They have waited for years.

The day the landmine exploded there was no paramedic. Period. The ambulance was a flatbed truck seconded into service. The road to a clinic was a treacherous pot-holed path where it might take two hours to travel fifty kilometers. Then two more hours on a paved road. The medical building did not have a state-of-the-art emergency care department. The 'Operating Room' might lack a surgeon and, even, essential supplies. Once a leg is severed there is no post-op plan for fitting a prosthetic leg. No prosthetic is coming. Not now, nor in the near future.

Florencia's situation had come to light by chance, not design. The chance was a conversation with some women demining and Katya Cengel. She had been on assignment in the region to research two stories: Women in Demining, and the widespread problem of 'Child Brides.' The women happened to mention an incident regarding a young single mother in a village to the north. A good journalist has an instinct, or nose, for a potential story. Katya definitely got the whiff of a drama worth investigating. She began to make further inquiries. She was advised to speak to a leader of the demining, Aderito Ismael. Aderito would have gladly taken Katya to Macachula, but, unfortunately, he needed to be at an important conference. However, he made all the arrangements for Katya, particularly organizing safe accommodation and transport for Katya. A more conscientious man would be hard to find. Katya undertook the arduous journey to Florencia's village. Days later she returned to California with the bones of two articles. The story included a few paragraphs, 217 words in all, describing Florencia, the landmine explosion, and her condition. Katya's article was not even included in the famous magazine edition of National Geographic. It was, however, inserted in the online edition.

So, the story that was unlikely to spread further than the few villages around the Massinga area was now circulating in cyberspace. It was a fortunate short inclusion in an online article. But, in all likelihood, Florencia's story would remain floating in internet space, and she would remain in her village, struggling on one leg and broken crutches - an accidental victim of the terrorist's cruel intentions. And that would be Florencia's lot, stuck, lame and unknown. That is until two men, whose lives had been rejuvenated and revitalized by ten days in Mozambique, decided to write a book. As part of their research, they looked up material on landmines. Google found Florencia. Luckily for Florencia, Douglas and John were more than readers and writers. Compelled by compassion and an outlandish idea they set out to get Florencia a leg. They found Aderito Ismael. Aderitio found Florencia. Google found DR Mehta. Now, from an accidental beginning, they were all in Jaipur, with one thing on their minds – to see Florencia walk.

In Dr. Pooja Mukul the team discovered more gold. They had found an expert in the mechanics of walking with a prosthetic and the therapy required. Florencia is one lucky girl. Ten Thousand of her compatriots wish they could have been so lucky. Without an assault of practical compassion, the willingness of so many to fund the project, and the generosity of Jaipur Foot, the skill of Dr. Pooja Mukul, this would not even have been a possibility.

But, Florencia was in Jaipur, and ready to face the challenge.

———

Chapter 22

Dancing With The Stars

Cinderella is proof that a new pair of shoes can change your life.

~Unknown

D
r. Mukul worked with surgical precision, and Florencia needed to adapt quickly to her new leg. The doctor taught Florencia how to walk again. Far from a 'just-strap-it-on-and-walk,' the process of fitting a prosthetic can be arduous. In fact, more often than not, it's extremely difficult. The physical therapy and re-training are crucial to the outcome and could make the difference between the amputee walking into a new future, or giving up and returning to the crutches. Often, the amputee has adapted to the crutches. This is a blessing and a curse. Florencia could move at quite a speed on her two supports, but there was a downside – the curse. She had accommodated her gait to the supports.

The consequences of this might be severe. Essentially, it meant she would need to unlearn any bad posture and poor ambulatory habits. Like all of us, Florencia's body was not designed to hop on crutches to get around. Leaning on these props while she washed, picked up firewood, and hoed the land may have been a source of admiration to all in her village, but the damage to her gait could make the prospects of walking with a new prosthetic problematic, to say the least. DR had been particularly nervous about Florencia's leg. Her above the knee amputation created its own set of issues. Not every amputation procedure is carried out under ideal conditions. He did not let on to John and Douglas these concerns.

Dr. Mukul, who was responsible for managing the fitting and therapy, would keep DR updated on Florencia's progress. The few days that Florencia would be in Jaipur and the reality that she was returning to the desolate bush of Mozambique, further complicated things.

Through the extreme generosity of the Hamlyn Foundation in London, Jaipur Foot has a state of the art walking and gait facility. Dr. Mukul could detect on her computer monitor the problems that Florencia was having and the bravery she demonstrated. Florencia gritted her teeth and did everything Dr. Mukul asked of her. But the Doctor knew the pain must have been excruciating. The outcome for the amputee hinged not merely on the professional skill and prowess of Dr. Mukul, but, also the capacity and dedication of Florencia. Occasionally, Douglas would pop into the walking room to check how things were going. Meanwhile, Culture Spark and the MAD students enjoyed the open access to all areas of Jaipur Foot. They were totally focused on creating media material, filming the production of Florencia's prosthetic. The MAD students also interviewed the Cal Poly students about their reactions to the prosthetic and initial impressions of the Jaipur Foot approach to helping the amputees.

Jaipur Foot's impressive work with above the knee amputees owes an awful lot to Stanford University in California. Several years ago a connection provided a tremendous boost for DR Mehta's work in Jaipur. That relationship was also somewhat accidental. It was the suggestion a driver chauffeuring DR Mehta around San Francisco. The result? The Stanford – Jaipur Foot Knee. Now produced by D-Rev, a company of engineers who had worked at Stanford on this project, this vital component enables the amputees to bend the leg to sit, walk, pray, work, and ride a bike. These are all key activities required in Indian culture.

"Douglas, hurry, bring everyone here. Florencia is ready to walk on her own."

These were the words that Douglas had longed to hear. He dashed into the interviewing session and informed the students that Dr. Mukul wanted them to come to the Walking Hall. Video cameras and still cameras at the ready, Florencia held Dr. Mukul's hands lightly, just to steady herself. No crutch. No walking stick. Dr. Mukul instructed Florencia to look straight ahead and keep looking ahead, like any normal person walks. Dr. Mukul let go of Florencia's grip, much like a parent lets go of the saddle when teaching a son or daughter to ride a bicycle. Within three or four steps the Princess of Mozambique was walking like royalty in front of adoring citizens. Occasionally, Florencia would be concerned and look down. Immediately, with a calm assurance, Dr. Mukul guided her protégé to look straight ahead. The student followed the advice and the regal walk returned. Florencia's eyes grew brighter with every step. She had done it - walked again. For those cheering and shooting footage, it was hard to take in. What on earth Florencia was thinking or feeling, nobody had the first idea. As if to underline the amazing efforts of Florencia, Dr. Mukul told Douglas and John of her observations of Florencia's work.

"She has done in two days what normally takes at least five days. Florencia has fought through her pain and the readjustments to her gait. She is a remarkable young woman."

Some of the students shot video. Others snapped photos. A few just watched.

The Cal Poly students went into deep conversation with Dr. Mukul about many of the technical aspects of the prosthetic and the problems Florencia had faced. Projects are important and the five Cal Poly Seniors threw themselves into learning all they could about the Jaipur prosthetic. Nevertheless, it is easy to lose sight of the person, the amputee, in all the data and interviews with the staff at Jaipur. Circumstances conspired to place one of the Cal Poly Seniors in an uncomfortable situation. It was an education of an altogether different kind. Kendall wrote of that moment.

'Leading up to the trip I was mostly in my own space, concerning myself with the engineering aspects of our project. Florencia was a client who represented the millions of landmine victims, but I was in very focused on the more technical side of things. Plus the idea of being in India and investigating the Jaipur foot fascinated me. When the male doctors were fitting the leg for Florencia, they needed a woman present in the room. For the previous days of the trip, Aderito's wife had been the woman present. That day though, she was not there and I happened to be the only girl in the area at the time. I was pulled into a room with Florencia and the two male doctors. I think they were having an issue with Florencia's prosthetic. Honestly, I'm not sure quite what the problem was. Aderito's wife spoke Portuguese and had been able to talk to Florencia who also spoke Portuguese. The doctors were making motions at me. They knew that I didn't speak Hindi, but I think they assumed, like Aderito's wife, I would be able to communicate with Florencia. I had no idea what they were trying to tell me. I couldn't communicate with them or Florencia. None of us spoke the same language. Confusion was written all over our faces.

Finally, through various hand motions, the doctors were able to attach the prosthetic. After which, they just left Florencia and me sitting next to each other, to wait for them to come back. It was kind of awkward. We hadn't really spent time together during the trip. The previous experience with the doctors was slightly uncomfortable. And it was just the two of us sitting practically shoulder to shoulder alone in a decently large room. The room was where Florencia had spent hours learning to walk on her new leg. This day was our final day, the leg she wore was the one she would wear to walk out of the Jaipur Foot later at the end of the day. She had also been given a brand new pair of shoes, which I am now realizing just the fact that it was shoes, plural, not just one, was a really big deal.

As we were sitting, not sure what to do, I put my feet together to examine the new brown 'tint' of my previously pure white Converse. Florencia must have watched me do this because, moments later, I watched her put her two shoes next to each other as well. I tilted my head to look up at her face. Her tears kissed her joyful smile. It was a smile as wide, and as deep, as the Grand Canyon, ear to ear. That's when the whole trip, the experience, the impact, finally, dawned on me. I had just put my feet together, spontaneously, without even a thought. It was just a natural thing to do. Florencia did this intentionally, as something she had not been able to do for so long. Two young *women in Jaipur, India checking out their footwear. Normal, right? The fact that it was just the two of us gave me the time to reflect in that moment. I had traveled for research, Florencia had traveled for a leg. Thoughts cascaded into my mind. I could not even begin to imagine my life without one of my legs. How could I even begin to understand the huge impact a new leg would have on Florencia's future. How hard the day to day tasks must have been. She had said she wanted to be able to dance with her son. Now, she would.*

We couldn't communicate, at least, verbally. But the serenity and pleasure she radiated, conveyed more than any words could. Sometimes people share unique and poignant moments with the catchphrase, 'you had to be there.' You know, I am so glad it was me, there, in that building, at that time, for that moment. It was then, and is now, a rare gift to treasure.'

Throughout the stay at the hotel, Rishu and Poovra were regularly asking how Florencia was doing. They not only exhibited excellent hospitality but seemed to enter into the dream of Florencia walking again. He may have been a young manager of a hotel but he was a man after Mehta's own heart. He had been rooting for Florencia all week, eagerly awaiting reports, almost as much as DR himself.

As the orange burnt sun set in the Indian sky, the Tuk-tuk pulled out of the Jaipur clinic parking lot and joined the already jam-packed Guru Nanak Path roadway. Aderito and Florencia were the sole occupants. They sat in silence during the ten-minute ride. Months earlier, Aderito had all but given up. He thought of that first day when they had met. A glaze came over his eyes. He had sat on a straw mat and read her a letter. A letter from two men he had never seen. Now they were friends for life. Today, a dream she could never have conceived was fulfilled. A dream he hadn't believed, had just happened. Spontaneous bubbles of delight blew over them. They were like children, all over again. Uninhibited tears, like a mountain river at the arrival of spring, rushed down their faces. They had both given everything to come this far – money, time, energy, faith, and months of working and waiting.

The sight of Florencia walking into the hotel was almost too much for Rishu. He wiped both eyes. After the evening meal on the last evening,

Rishu gathered everyone into the lounge area. Florencia sat in her new posture – a royal one, back straight and eyes shining like diamonds. A convivial atmosphere of delightful lightheartedness was everywhere. And everyone caught the mood.

Here, tonight, in a hotel in Jaipur, India the dream and the dreamers were sitting together on a couch. For some reason, the lights were dimmed. In walked Rishu and Poovra bearing their gift to Florencia, a rich chocolate layer cake, beautifully iced with white frosting and topped with a set of bright-burning sparklers.

White icing had artistically piped,

A MOST BEAUTIFUL DAY FLORENCIA

Florencia's face lit up, reflecting the burning candles on the cake. She let out a girlish laugh and, almost immediately, everyone joined in. There was an unmistakable air of relief and joy. In the middle of the raucous celebration, Aderito leaned over and asked Florencia if she had eaten any cake like that before. She hadn't. He didn't need to ask whether she liked the cake. Three things told him the answer. The empty plate had been licked clean in record time. Blobs of pale cream icing painted her cheeks, and the princess from Africa had a perfect set of dark chocolate teeth.

Later that night, on a candlelit rooftop of a hotel in Jaipur, in near perfect English, a young woman from a village in the bush of Mozambique asked a disco-loving hotel manager to dance. Douglas, who also taught English, told everyone that Florencia obviously could excel in languages, with the right teacher, of course.

Earlier in the evening, Poovra had let it be known her brother was a brilliant dancer. She was not wrong.

With all eyes on the Mozambique dancer, Rishu launched into a Bollywood special. In seconds Florencia's body swayed and moved. Along with the equally, vivacious Victoria, Florencia showed the rest of the team the rhythms of Africa were alive once again. She didn't move far, but everyone knew, she had come a long, long way.

Adrianne Haslet-Davis would have been proud of this African Princess.

Chapter 23

Headwinds

When everything seems to be going against you,
remember that the airplane takes off against the wind, not with it.

~Henry Ford

A ir travel changed for everyone. Permanently. Before September 11, 2001, flying was truly a pleasure, well most of the time. Frank Sinatra's famous crooning of Jimmy Van Heusen's 1958 upbeat classic says it all, "Come fly with me."

Come fly with me, let's fly, let's fly away…

Once I get you up there,

Where the air is rarefied,

We'll just glide,

Starry-eyed,

Once I get you up there,

I'll be holding you so near.

Back then, you could stroll right through airport security without removing your shoes. A contented traveler might be humming Frank's song.

A laptop rested safely in a backpack. A man's belt was secure in the hoops of his pants. Every size of liquid was left untouched in the overnight bag. The greatest inconvenience was fumbling through pockets to grab loose change, in order to pass through the metal detector. Friends and family could even meet at the departure gate. Flying was fun, back in the day.

Even the airplane cockpit was accessible. In 1975, Douglas, a young 24-year-old was en route from Heathrow Airport in London to JFK in New York. It was his first-ever flight. A stewardess came down the aisle. She tapped a little boy seated in front of Douglas on the shoulder. "Would you like to go and see the pilot?" The boy jumped out of his seat. Douglas inquired, "Can a big boy accompany him?" Both 'boys' were escorted into the cockpit, warmly greeted by the captain and his co-pilot, and shown how the instruments and controls helped fl y the plane. Each was left with a memento – a set of 'junior pilot wings. As Louis Armstrong would croon, 'It's a wonderful world.'

And then, the Twin Towers came down, along with the sheer innocent delight of flying the 'friendly skies.'

Pilots were now locked behind impregnable doors sealed shut for the full duration of the flight. The cabin door didn't even need a 'no visitor' sign. Everyone knew there was no access. Friends couldn't gather and chat in any part of a plane. Just in case there was an incident, a fully armed undercover federal air marshal was on board and prepared to react to any inflight threat.

Soon after 9/11, the Federal Government created the Transportation Security Administration (TSA) for the purpose of screening all passengers. In the 'new normal,' flyers must arrive at the airport two hours before their flight. Vehicles can only drop passengers off at the curbside. If you're parked more than two minutes an unfriendly policeman will approach you and wave you off. And don't leave a bag unattended for even a few seconds. It could be gone. Not taken by a light-fi ngered thief, but by a zealous security agent.

After winding the way like a centipede through a long, serpentine waiting line a sign awaits the traveler at the checkpoint. It presents every passenger with their immediate 'To Do' list. Please remove your jacket, shoes, belt, computer, and quart-size bag for liquid, aerosols, gels, and creams. The slow process grinds to a halt as each person's body is patted down, scanned, and possibly, subject to a small-scale strip down. Each passenger checks their ruffled clothing, ties their shoes, locates their personal bags, and wipes their brow. Finally, they can relax until called to the gate.

Yes, it's all so different now. It's the high cost we pay to be safe. The extra security has literally come with a price tag. Luggage in the hold is upwards of $25 per bag. Some bloggers have made a business out of demonstrating how much you can pack, cram and squeeze into a carry-on. Flying today is a chore. And for some passengers, it can be one gigantic, royal pain.

John and the team left Jaipur hours after Aderito, Victoria, Stephane, and Florencia. They arranged to meet up in Addis Ababa for the final leg to Maputo, Mozambique. It was a very tight connection, As soon as they landed at Ethiopia's capital the team were whisked away in a bus, direct to the Maputo bound plane. They didn't even enter the Terminal. As they inched their way to the economy section they heard Aderito, "Hey John, Douglas." Florencia had a row to herself and Aderito, Victoria and Stephane were in the row behind. Once airborne, and the seat belt sign was off, Douglas made his way up the aisle to Florencia and took a photo of the glowing, young, African woman. As one who loves to teach English, Douglas taught Florencia a few phrases. The girl from the bush displayed a natural aptitude for the Commonwealth mother tongue. It didn't take too much imagination to realize this mother could hardly wait to get home to see her son, Guildo. She could take a walk with him, hand in hand.

Douglas casually asked Aderito how the flights had gone. It was one of those throwaways which expected an assessment of the food and the relative comfort of the seats, and not much more. Aderito made no mention of either topic in his, very full, reply.

"You thought a couple of Walkie Talkies were a problem in Dubai. That's nothing – a piece of cake. Try traveling with an amputee with two prosthetic legs and brand new crutches. The security check for the Addis Ababa flight was a nightmare. It was an anniversary of a terrorist attack in India and security was reinforced everywhere. Florencia was made to take her prosthesis off. For about one hour Victoria tried to understand the Indian English dialect and transmit the meaning to Florencia. It seemed dealing with the prosthetic was new for everyone. At last, we embarked for Addis. As far as I could see an awful lot of African people had been in India for medical treatment, and Addis Ababa was the connection airport. Our plane back looked like one giant ambulance."

Aderito's turn of phrase was always liable to bring a smile, even when reporting on, what had undoubtedly been, a very frustrating experience.

Aderito's comments did lead to Douglas understanding the kind of issues that an amputee faces, even if they are fortunate to have a prosthesis. In a November 2010 article in *Popular Mechanics*, Tyghe Trimble provides a glimpse into the world of the amputee traveler.

'You're flying home to visit the parents for Thanksgiving – a short flight, some 500 miles away. You arrive at the airport 90 minutes early – it is, after all, holiday travel season. After showing your ID and boarding pass, you get to the screening area. You pull out your laptop – and your iPad, just because – and place them in separate bins. You walk through a backscatter scanner and get the wand. Judging by the looks of the TSA employees and the constant beeping, you're not passing either test. "You see," you try to explain to them, "I'm wearing prosthetic legs. I'm handicapped."

This is where the process slows down. Swabs are taken immediately, in and around all prosthetics to detect for bomb-making material. Then you wait. The next step is to go under the CastScope. Sometimes there is a certified employee on the premises. But often, you have to wait for employees to hunt one down. Once the operator is found, you go under the machine, prosthetic limbs still on. They take X-ray images on the front, back and sides – about 10 X-rays per below-the-knee prosthetic, more if your prosthesis has a mechanical knee. After these X-rays pass inspection, you're free to fly.'

The problem for the amputee, with a prosthetic, is seriously compounded by the variety of interpretations of the guidelines and protocols.

Thankfully the Amputee Coalition is working diligently on behalf of amputees.

Trimble goes on to note, 'A survey of 7300 amputee passengers showed that travelers with limb loss have been subjected to inconsistent, unfair, abusive and often embarrassing screenings by security employees.' Perhaps greater attention and prioritizing for these passengers could make their already difficult trip easier. It certainly should make the able-bodied grateful and patient.

If anyone had taken notice of Florencia – it would have been quite a spectacle to behold – Florencia walking on two legs and carrying the third with two crutches in tow. That day three legs passed through immigration and customs at the Maputo International Airport. The sleep-deprived entourage climbed on board a twenty passenger transit van bound for Zimpeto Children's Center.

The Zimpeto Children Center welcomed the team with open arms. Typical of what John had found thirteen years earlier, they gave everything and asked for nothing. John, Douglas, and Dan went to the shops to get some supplies for dinner and breakfast. The hungry travelers devoured the dinner, washed up and had an early night. The next morning, after a quick breakfast the team were packed and waiting for Aderito to come with Florencia. He and a friend would drive the sport utility vehicles to a lodge near Macachula.

The center was swarming with those lovable African children one sees in magazines and documentaries. Whatever their trials they exuded pure joy and the occasional sneaky trick. Once again the skills and talents of the team came to the fore. Luke and Tanner were entertaining a few boys with non-stop soccer. The media guys were thrilling some others, demonstrating the video and still cameras. Douglas thought, *what could be done if America sent these teams for longer periods, to inspire these boys and girls in sports, media, language and music?* All it takes is a strategy, some funds, and an ongoing commitment.

Eventually, the vehicles arrived, the gear was packed in and lots of short black arms waved farewell. A few ran behind the vehicles all the way to the gate of the Center.

The convoy sped away northwards on Route 1. Massinga was 530 kilometers away, and then there would be the scary, last 50 kilometers to Macachula. Aderito reminded everyone it was critical to make it by dusk. Any delays would mean arriving in the dark, and that, as they knew, would be inadvisable. It was the same advice Aderito had given Katya Cengel's driver when taking her to interview Florencia and her mother, Guilda.

The journey went well for all of thirty kilometers. Then Aderito fell foul to one of those concealed speed traps, doing 70 in a 60 zone provoked a policeman to flag down the vehicle. The other vehicle passed the policeman talking to Aderito, and slowed to a stop, about 100 meters beyond the police. They watched and waited. Suddenly there was some hectic activity, and the next scene saw Ben get out of Aderito's SUV. Apparently, he had thought it would be a great opportunity to take some video of the event. It was not a good idea.

For the next thirty to forty minutes, it was touch and go as to whether the police would confiscate the very expensive camera, and, or, drive Ben and Aderito away. Initially, it was somewhat humorous until everyone realized the police were not laughing and neither was Ben nor Aderito. Now, it was tense, in the extreme. What the team could not hear was that the Police were thinking they would take everybody to the Police Station. Ben got on his knees, begged and pleaded with the officer just to take him alone, that nothing of consequence was on film and that he, Ben, could not be sorrier. There was a lengthy pause. Aderito got out his wallet and told the officer that he would pay whatever fine was necessary. The vehicles drove off, everyone relieved and the drivers careful of their speed, and with eyes peeled for other speed guns.

Despite stopping only to fill up with petrol, and a brief break for lunch, dusk descended long before the right hand turn off from Route 1, just beyond Massinga. The undulating path ended at the beach on the Indian Ocean. Dusk turned into a dark African night faster than Douglas could say, "How far is it to Macachula, Aderito?" For a moment Aderito was quiet. He was trying, in vain, to steer the SUV along a narrow, treacherous, sandy path. When he could finally see a stretch of path the length of a tennis court, he answered, " It's 58 kilometers, but when it is as black as coal, it is not the distance that is the problem. It's the fact you can be lost so quickly, and every path seems the same." Douglas didn't respond. Aderito's tone said enough. One didn't need a degree in discernment to realize this was no time for humor. Douglas kept the lid on the funny comment that was on the tip of his quick tongue. The plan was to stay the night in chalets at the Lodge and then drive Florencia home in the morning. The night took on the atmosphere of night maneuvers in an army boot camp. It reminded John of a car rally in the forest, only there was only one car in this forest.

One hour of bumpy heads-hit-the-roof-of-the-SUV went by. When one was avoiding the concussion one concentrated on keeping the contents of the stomach, in the stomach. Off road rallying at speed may be okay for a bit of fun and a giggle. After two hours everyone was tired and nerves were beginning to be frayed at the edges. Of course, nobody on the team could help, except to refrain from offering any smart comments. Aderito did manage to get hold of the manager of the Lodge on the phone, but there were so few features that could let the manager know Aderito's location. The Manager had already sent out a search patrol on foot. Where they were, nobody knew. They drove around, and around. They stopped. They drove some more. They stopped. They called again. Nothing.

This last few kilometers were much like the entire mission – an exercise in determination and endurance, overcoming seemingly never-ending obstacles and delays. When all seemed completely lost, the path to the

Lodge found the vehicles. The unmistakable salt air filled the nostrils, and the outside light of the Lodge shone, albeit dimly, through the night sea mist. Everyone was dog tired, yet buzzing with adrenaline. Sleep might not be as easy to come by tonight. They had not taken into account the sound of the waves. The gentle sound of the lapping Indian Ocean quickly induced a sense of calm and much needed rest. It was fortunate for the team that Douglas read a book for a few minutes. His snoring is legendary. The team woke up in paradise. Each member crawled out from under their white veils, as John christened them. These were the familiar protective mosquito nets that completely covered each sleeper. The sun was shining. The daylight revealed the rooms were barely ten meters away from an idyllic sandy beach at the edge of a lagoon. The breakfast served at the Lodge was awarded five stars by everyone, eggs, bacon, cereal, fresh fruit, toast, rolls, and lashings of hot coffee and tea.

John and Douglas could envisage incorporating a few months at the Lodge into their new career as writers. This would be the ideal place to write a book. No internet. No phones. No interruptions. All the time in the world to walk, create and write. A writer's heaven, well at least for a few months, until island fever set in, or a serious case of writer's block.

Dane and Samsun had planned out their day. They would have only one day to shoot Florencia's homecoming, with other footage and stills of Florencia's hut and the location where the landmine had exploded. Ben and Brett had their own menu for the material they wanted to produce. A last minute check ensured the cameras, microphones, and the, now infamous, walkie talkies were charged and loaded into the SUV.

Florencia seemed calm, but pensive. No doubt her mind must have bounced from reflection to anticipation. Neither she, nor her village, could have imagined this day would come. How would Guildo react to his mother without crutches? All he'd ever known was a mother with less than half a right leg and big sticks to help her get around.

Chapter 24

The Cashew Tree

A cashew nut causes anyone who sees it to turn into an orchid.

~Anonymous

The drive from the Lodge to Florencia's village brought some magnificent views of the pristine coastline. Anyone who has the good fortune to set their eyes on the aqua blue waters of the Indian Ocean can instantly 'feel' the beauty. The SUV stopped to allow the media guys shots of the lagoon, and beyond to the waves pounding the beach. From the crest of the headland the vehicles descended into the bush. It was immediately easy to understand why the drivers had lost their way the previous night. Every area looks identical, a few trees and scattered mud huts. The drive was made slightly easier because the numerous potholes in the sandy track could now be seen. The previous night they had been invisible until the last moment, often too late for the driver to avoid them.

Florencia was quiet for the twenty-five-minute journey to her village.

Right now, in the final few kilometers to her village, she probably wondered how her mother was doing. Aderito had offered her some money to go to see a doctor. It was, politely, refused. Florencia was glad her grandmother and some other young mothers were there to help with Guildo. What could be worse than a young mother concerned for the health of her own mother, and leaving her son to fly into the unknown? Gut wrenching, and thousands of miles away, with no way to communicate. In John and Douglas's conversations, they had marveled at the young woman's fortitude. Maybe the hard work Florencia had to put in with Dr. Mukul had, somehow, actually been a help. The pain was fierce, but it was a distraction from the inner concerns. Now all of that was in the past. A new future had arrived.

The SUV rolled up and stopped on the sandy soil of Macachula. Florencia was home.

The media team were ahead, in position. Aderito opened the Toyota door, and Florencia stepped out. She paused, and inhaled, deeply. She needed to, for the sight which met her was one to take the breath away. Macachula had turned out in force. Men, women, and children gathered to see the return of their Florencia. Members of the small church were there. Children ran around in packs, playing. Florencia walked toward the 'Uncles' of the Village. These were the community and church elders. She shook the hand of each and every man to the sound of African songs ascending to the heavens. The haunting melodies were captivating. Dane, camera rolling, had never heard or seen anything quite like these local women. They were a collage of color, as if angels had just splashed every combination imaginable on the ladies of Macachula. They sang like angels too. It was like the set of a well-crafted movie where the audience knows this is a true story. This was one of those spine-chilling, goosebumps producing, moments. Florencia greeted every woman, with radiant joy. The songs went on and on, rising in crescendos, then quietly, fading to whispered harmonies. Nobody wanted them to stop.

Loud or soft, it unlocked the heart. Another tear duct opening moment was Guildo reunited with his mother. Initially, the scene was hilarious. Guildo looked incredulous. His mother on two legs? He ran away in the opposite direction. What must the little boy have been thinking? With some coaxing and encouragement, it wasn't long before curiosity and love won him over. This was such a fresh experience – carried around by his own mother – one of the many great sights that day.

Greetings were shared by the Elder of the Community and the leader of the Church. Translators were present and needed. English, Portuguese and the local dialect were spoken. Aderito emphasized Florencia's courage and the trust that the whole village had placed in him, a relative stranger, with the wild plan, to borrow Florencia for seven days and take her across the ocean to a clinic, in the hope of receiving a leg. Tanner and Landon spoke warmly and eloquently of their trip to India, and the welcome by the villagers of Macachula. John followed, sharing a couple of unforgettable stories and appreciation of all who had shared in the mission. Then, unexpectedly, the formerly shy, withdrawn, somewhat sad girl stood up on two legs. The air crackled with electricity and expectation. And then, to the surprise of many, Florencia stood up and spoke. If it was totally unexpected, what followed was, exceptional.

Her voice resounded with such clarity and confidence. Frankly, it amazed everyone. Every word was absorbed. She thanked the village for encouraging her to go, even though it was with more faith than certainty. Florencia told of how she traveled in fear, but also in hope. She thanked them for their prayers. It was a declaration, much more than a simple, nervous, young girl. This was a woman exuberant and in total command of the crowd. She told them of the moment when she saw a small, elderly man who had moved so quickly, stop and take off one prosthetic, and then the other. That was when she knew she could do it, walk again. Florencia, with a face as bright as the sun thundered out a closing "I did it!" The volume of the clapping seemed to echo with a resounding: "That's our girl, Florencia!"

The Elder of the church asked if anyone could bring a short sermon. John suggested Douglas. From thinking that there was nothing left to say, Douglas had to think quickly. He launched a text message to the sky. Inspiration spoke and Douglas simply passed on the message.

"HOW has been formed because John and I were moved deeply by Florencia's story. We put down our book because a young woman needed a better ending to a tragedy. We started HOW to literally, Help One Walk. What a marvelous day for Florencia and all of you here, today. Florencia walked into this village on two feet, with a pair of brand new shoes. Actually, she has two pairs of shoes. It has taken an American journalist, two writers, one from California, America, and one from Britain, a Mozambican deminer and his wife, an elderly man from India, with the spirit of Mahatma Gandhi, a village of faith, and a tenacious, determined young woman to do the impossible. People from three continents imagined a fresh future for a stranger, a young mother of Macachula.

Why did we do this? All because of a simple truth thousands of years old. Many know it as the Golden Rule.

Do unto others as you would have them do unto you.

Suppose John's daughter or my daughter had lost a leg and we did not have the resources to help her, we'd like to think that somebody would help us. Well, we heard about Florencia. She didn't know where to get a leg, and neither did we, but when you know of the need you are ruined. You must do something, and stop at nothing until it is done. And now we want to tell her story in a book.

Why, you may ask?

So that 10,000 others, others like Florencia, can walk again. It took people on three continents to get this done, But, if you are willing, you will find a way. Not everyone could come on this mission. But it doesn't matter if it was a child giving one dollar, a person who gave $5,000 dollars, an artist creating a poster, or a student making a video, or you welcoming Aderito into Florencia's life. So, don't think of this mission as all about us. It is not.

If your neighbor is sick and you make some soup and take it to him, it's the golden rule in action. Wouldn't this kindness change the world? Jesus thought so. Let's all embrace this golden rule, 'Do to others what you would have them do to you.' God bless you all and thank you for allowing us to take this wonderful Princess of Africa to India. Today is a day of joyful celebration."

Douglas led everyone in a prayer of thanksgiving and said, "We have one more thing to do. Aderito would like to take us to the site of where it all began."

A crowd gathered at the scene of the tragedy.

Aderito described the scene and the story. He took the graphic pencil from behind his ear and drew an impromptu map on the ground. He then pointed to the brow of the hill. "If you stood on the top and look down towards the ocean, you'd see the lodge where we had breakfast. It was natural for the Frelimo to protect the headland. They wanted to see rebel soldiers coming. There was a series of mines there, ten meters apart."

"You can probably imagine the two Frelimo soldiers crawling on their stomachs and dragging their backpacks with their devices down to where we're standing. They must have known there was a good chance an innocent villager would die."

When we came to de-mine, we immediately located the crater where Florencia had her accident. You can see it, there. It's about a meter wide. Some of the students took shots of the crater.

He then pointed a few feet away. "There was another mine there. A more dangerous mine with a rocket booster."

Someone asked, "What if she had stepped on that mine?"

"She'd be dead." Nothing further needed to be said. A deafening silence stopped any whispering conversation.

"We demined that one and we removed two more a few meters away." Aderito raised his head. In less than a few seconds, his penetrating eyes went around the whole group.

"There's one major reason why I've brought you here."

"You'll remember that Florencia came to collect firewood. On the way, she reached up to grab a couple of cashews. She dropped them into the breast pocket of her blouse."

"When the mine blew up under her feet somehow those two cashews landed under her body in the center of this crater.

"Those two cashews somehow found their way into the soil." "Look." The ex-army deminer choked on the word, but pointed to the crater. Aderito's listeners looked at a cashew tree, about five feet high. It was perfectly centered in the crater, as if by design.

Aderito continued, but in little more than a whisper.

"When Florencia first saw this little tree, it became a source of comfort. I visited her one day and we came to this site. She hobbled here on crutches and showed me this tree, and told me about the cashews in her blouse pocket. This Cashew tree is no ordinary tree to Florencia. It is full of significance and meaning.

Once this was a crater of grief. Now, Florencia believes the growth of this cashew tree is a sign to her, maybe the work of God, or an angel. She will walk here with Guildo. Florencia will come to this place, and tell her son about her India, and her journey to Jaipur. We, as Africans love our stories, and this is one I would never have believed possible. I think it will become a regular bedtime story - can you hear Guildo, 'Tell me the tale of the Cashew tree and your leg, please mummy?' It is a sacred place and this tree is the sign of a miracle."

The team lingered and then dispersed with a subdued, hushed, respectful silence.

Florencia posed for a few final photos. Arguably, on that day at least, Florencia had been the most photographed model in Mozambique. The sun slipped below the brow of the headland. Dusk beckoned the night sky. But first , under the tapestry of the vermillion, blue and blood orange glow, Florencia, minus her wooden supports, wandered slowly, her white sneakers leaving gentle imprints in the sand. Florencia, minus her wooden supports, wandered into the field in her new white shoes. She had been caught up in a whirlwind. How could she describe it? Transported to places far away and to meet people unknown. This flower had been to the moon and back, at least it must have seemed that way. Now she was here on familiar ground, no longer standing in a place of pain. In the silence, the birds sang a new evensong. To Florencia, the lyrical melody chirped, 'welcome home little flower, we missed you, welcome home.' The sea of red had been transformed into a sea of tranquility. Florencia breathed in deep, deep, breaths of peace.

In the cool afternoon shade she stood tall and elegant,
A beautiful orchid beside her very own cashew tree.

Epilogue

Epilogue

They say timing is everything...It certainly turned out to be true in our story. How quickly the thrill of a great moment is smothered by the sadness of a tragic loss. We returned from Mozambique to Santa Barbara on December 2, 2015, ready and eager to make plans for Florencia's 10,000 fellow amputees to receive legs and walk again. Within a few days of returning, Luke O'Neil's mother passed away, and just one week later Aderito emailed us with the news that Florencia's mother, Guilda, had died. Needless to say, we were heartbroken for these two young people.

The effect of the death of the one person who brought us into the world cannot be fathomed until it is experienced. At the age of eighteen, it can be devastating. Our hearts mourned with them in their loss. Yet, even in the darkest of experiences, a ray of light can shine. A dying mother in Santa Barbara had lived to see her son fulfill a dream she had held on to since his boyhood days. To go to Africa. Thousands of miles away in the bush of Mozambique an ailing mother of Florencia had lived to see her daughter walk again on two legs.

It was a sobering thought when we realized just how close we had come to postponing the mission. Taking everything into consideration it could have been seen as a wise choice. The major motivating force to drive on, regardless of obstacles, was the thought of Florencia, on broken crutches stumbling through life. Only in January 2016 did we begin to tap into the mystery of timing. To paraphrase an ancient sage, to everything there is a time, a time to postpone, and a time to move heaven and hell to go. For us, Thanksgiving 2015 was the time to go. We planned, dared, risked, and we went. And we are so thankful we did.

A Call To Action

Dear Reader,

It has been our privilege to share this book with you. Both of us are still learning what it means to Stop for the One. We hope you have enjoyed 'Florencia, An Accidental Story.'

The story continues…After receiving a prosthetic leg, Florencia has traveled back to Jaipur with three other Mozambicans to become a trained prosthetic technician. All four are spending three months at the Jaipur Clinic, training in all aspects of fabrication and fitting of prosthetic legs. Just getting them there has been a fresh drama filled with many twists and turns. The excitement and challenge is entering a new chapter.

Many of you have asked, 'How can I help?'

As we move into this next phase to support Florencia and her friends, our goal is to help each of them walk again whether it be furthering their education, finding gainful employment, or properly caring for their family.

So, what are some of the ways in which you can help, now and in the long term?

Help support a Mobile Medical Lab to fabricate and fit prosthetic limbs.

Make a difference by giving a leg or making a monthly/annual investment long term.

To Donate, you can send a check to:
HOW Internattiional
949 Veronica Springs Road
Santa Barbara, CA 93109
https://helponewalk.givingfuel.com/help10000walk

To Give a Leg or make a one-time donation, follow the link:
https://helponewalk.givingfuel.com/help10000walk

Reflection

Dear John and Douglas,

I love the book! I cried at least a dozen times and laughed out loud on four occasions.

The opening scene in the munitions factory was brilliant. Culprits come in all shapes and sizes, as do angels. I like the funny and yet revealing intro to John and Doug. The human story on several continents was engrossing. The short yet strong chapters that built together were a really enticing, enabling continuation of reading.

I liked the spiritual dimension that evolved with the human story. There were some great spiritual concepts that were extremely powerful. I loved the quotes that popped up across the story.

I particularly like the way you told the story of the main characters, yourselves, Florencia, Aderito and DR Mehta. There is a great balance of humor, pathos, tragedy, heroics and passion. It is a riveting storyline. The way you linked tragedy and devastation with opportunity, trust and faith.

The book showcases the roller coaster ride involved in getting a project off the ground. It takes a village from around the world demonstrating that projects are as much about relationships being developed as the objective being fulfilled.

I loved the sense of how things can change and circumstances fluctuate and what that can create. A flood raising awareness across the other side of the world, a woman being prompted to return to work and make sure passports would be sent out on time, the elation and prayer at every turn with people partnering above and beyond the norm.

This is not just a book about a girl's tragic story and the way people she had never met fought for her to overcome. It's also a manual about receiving favor and the practice of focus and fortitude required to get a cause off the ground. The hunger to stop at nothing until an objective is achieved.

I loved the wisdom that is liberally sprinkled throughout the storytelling. Justice and faith cannot be separated. Overcoming obstacles provides us with the strength within to rise up against any adversity and overwhelm it! Giving out of guilt lacks substance, but love transforms the giver. Not condescending compassion but compassionate solidarity. A good person is one who senses the pain of another.

Great ideas must of necessity be confronted by negativity and discouragement. This empowers people to become more inventive and creative. In this way a dream or idea can increase and be realized at a higher level. Justice is writing a wrong. Compassion is the demonstration of practical love.

Delay and obstruction empower us to hold our nerve. The concept of the artistry of grace that finds beauty in everyone and goodness in everything. Be a friend to the least. All wonderful words of love, hope and the wisdom that can be discovered in every circumstance if we could prevent ourselves from being fearful and worrying.

The quotes were remarkable. Nobody is superior, nobody is inferior, and nobody is equal either. People are simply unique and incomparable. VIP's = Very Important Poor!...brilliant!

My favorite quote from Henry Ford, "when everything seems to be going against you, remember that the airplane takes off against the wind, not with it."

Involving MAD and creating viral support and promotion of the project is genius. Developing organizational and logistical favor. Finding the people to drive it forward in every area requires a deep sense of stewardship not ownership. Allowing people to contribute without controlling the process…that's really smart.

I liked the way the stories of a Brit and an American ebbed and flowed from the forefront to the background. This book really is a training manual in how to get things done against the odds.

It is an excellent book. My respect and love for both of you has grown considerably.

Well done!

Graham Cooke
President, Brilliant Perspectives

Acknowledgements

This journey has been a chapter of accidents. However, without the good intentions of so many family and friends, this book might not have been written, and certainly not finished. So much of the content of this book would not have appeared were it not for the hundreds of supporters who helped Florencia get a leg, enabled students to travel, and attended and gave at HOW events. There's a host of HOW followers to whom we are indebted. Florencia walks because we all pulled together and made it happen.

To the dozens of student supporters and interns at MAD Academy and Cal Poly: we both salute you and everything you have done. Take a bow and let's keep the good going. You stopped for the one, but we will not stop at one.

Special thanks to Hank Bowis and John Davies who have literally held our hand, encouraged, cajoled and given of their resources. We had so many who financially have come alongside in this book project including; Melanie Cava and Todd Drevo, William and Sue Davies, and Paul and Carolyn Aijian.

We deeply appreciate Bestseller Publishing, particularly the inspiration of Rob Kosberg and the tireless editing of Sydney Hubbard. Your team is awesome! Laura Bowman wrote the powerful prologue and gave countless hours to ensuring the quality of the manuscript and the consistency of the story.

Dan Williams, for your vision and leadership of the MAD Academy students, we are so very grateful. You boldly stepped up to give them this opportunity. They gave themselves and their incredible talents to reach out to Florencia. Her story has become a MAD story, and she now wears a MAD Academy baseball cap to shade her eyes in the Macachula sun.

For the depth of experience and passion in the Forward by President Chissano we could not have hoped for a better platform to launch Florencia's story. For the friendship and advice along the way, and the brilliant Reflection, Graham you're the best! Dr. Leonardo Simão, you are an agent of compassion whose unwavering service to the people of Mozambique is clearly evident. Your work with the Chissano Foundation is supporting HOW at a level we had never imagined.

The kind endorsements by DR Mehta, Billy Baldwin, Melanie Cava, Dr. Jeffrey Armstrong, Nick Vujicic, and Dr. John Bechhio have motivated us to carry this story to the world.

Dedications

To the two most deserving women we know
Kim Mullen & Fiona Bowman

To our children Nicole, Connor, Preston, Landon, Barrie, and Laura
You have always been and continue to be a source of constant inspiration

To two Mozambican champions, Aderito de Jesus Ismael and
Victoria Papadakis

You adopted Florencia as if she were your very own daughter
We count you as true friends